Core Books in Advanced M

Proof

C. Plumpton
Moderator in Mathematics, University of
London School Examinations Department;
formerly Reader in Engineering Mathematics,
Queen Mary College, University of London.

R. L. Perry, Ph.D.
University Assistant Moderator in Advanced-level Mathematics,
University of London School Examinations Department;
Senior Lecturer in Pure Mathematics,
Queen Elizabeth College, University of London.

E. Shipton
Teacher-moderator in Advanced-level Mathematics,
University of London School Examinations Department;
formerly Deputy Head, Owen's School, Potters Bar.

Macmillan Education
London and Basingstoke

First published 1984

Published by
Macmillan Education Limited
Houndmills Basingstoke Hampshire RG21 2XS
and London
Associated companies throughout the world

Typeset in Hong Kong by Asco Trade Typesetting Ltd.
Printed in Hong Kong

ISBN 0 333 86717 0

Contents

Contents

Preface

Advanced level mathematics syllabuses are once again undergoing changes of content and approach, following the revolution in the early 1960s which led to the unfortunate dichotomy between 'modern' and 'traditional' mathematics. The current trend in syllabuses for Advanced level mathematics now being developed and published by many GCE boards is towards an integrated approach, taking the best of the topics and approaches of the modern and traditional, in an attempt to create a realistic examination target through syllabuses which are maximal for examining and minimal for teaching. In addition, resulting from a number of initiatives, core syllabuses are being developed for Advanced level mathematics consisting of techniques of pure mathematics as taught in schools and colleges at this level.

The concept of a core can be used in several ways, one of which is mentioned above, namely the idea of a core syllabus to which the options, such as theoretical mechanics, further pure mathematics and statistics can be added. The books in this series are core books involving a different use of the core idea. They are books on a range of topics each of which is central to the study of Advanced level mathematics. The books also form small core studies of their own, of topics which, together, cover the main areas of any single-subject mathematics syllabus at Advanced level.

The series will be found particularly valuable at times when economic conditions create acute problems in the acquisition of comprehensive textbooks giving complete syllabus coverage. Schools, colleges and individual students can collect as many of the core books as they need to supplement books they already possess, so that the most recent syllabuses of, for example, the London, Cambridge, AEB and JMB GCE Boards, can be covered at minimum expense. Alternatively, of course, the whole set of core books gives complete syllabus coverage of single-subject Advanced level mathematics.

The aim of each book is to develop a major topic of the single-subject syllabuses. All essential bookwork is given, together with worked examples and exercises arising from the authors' vast experience of examining at this level. Many questions of GCE Advanced level type are also included. Thus, the core books, as well as being used in the ways described above, would also be ideal for supplementing comprehensive textbooks by providing more examples and exercises, so necessary for preparation and revision for examinations on the Advanced level mathematics syllabuses offered by the GCE Boards.

The subject of this volume of the series is mathematical proof. During the early years at secondary school, any sort of formal proof in mathematics is no longer required of pupils. Gone are the days of the geometry theorem carefully written down and learnt (often by heart!). Instead, the time is spent on familiarising the pupils with new concepts and on the acquisition of skills in dealing with those concepts. However, at the later stages of a mathematics course and certainly at sixth-form level, the formal proof, that is the carefully reasoned argument, is necessary and it is not always realised what difficulties this presents to students. Whilst textbooks introduce proofs of various kinds at this level, very little is said about the nature of the process and of the various forms that it can take. Thus, what is often seen as a proof by students is a sequence of statements, often relevant, but lacking the necessary connectives to constitute a proof. When, therefore, it comes to a particular form of proof, for example mathematical induction, where the correct reasoning is absolutely crucial to the argument, students tend to find great difficulty. All too often, examiners find that perfectly correct statements are put together invalidly to give a 'proof' that does not even make sense.

The present book has been written in an attempt to help sixth-form teachers and students by discussing the nature of proof and by setting out the various forms of proof which are available. Experience shows that first-year university students could also profit from a study of this book. Many proofs are given in full for the guidance of students and there are numerous examples for them to work. These include many of the more sophisticated types of multiple-choice items which are found in some Advanced level mathematics papers nowadays. It is hoped, therefore, that the book will be valuable to many university students and to all A-level students and their teachers.

Examples in the book which are suitable for candidates doing double-subject mathematics or pure mathematics only are marked with an asterisk and those suitable for candidates doing applied mathematics are marked with two asterisks.

Finally, we should like to thank the following who were kind enough to read through the manuscript for us and give us the benefit of their advice although, in some cases, we persisted in our ways despite their protests: Prof. C. W. Kilmister, Prof. T. J. Wilmore, Dr Mary Tropper, Laurence Pateman, Michael Kenwood, David Thorning, David Taylor, Pamela Masters, Vivienne Lawson, John Harber, Heather Abbott, Dr Tony Asher, Dr A. R. Pears, Dr J. Hebborn, Hugh Neill. We are doubly grateful to Prof. C. A. Rogers FRS who not only read the manuscript and made valuable suggestions, but also wrote chapter 8 on the use of English by mathematicians. Frank Dobby drew the cartoons.

C. Plumpton
R. L. Perry
E. Shipton

1 What is proof?

1.1 Introduction

Among other things, mathematics deals with numbers, symbols, operations, spatial properties and problem solving. Since earliest times the subject has been developed by mathematicians having an intuitive feeling that some proposition is true and then demonstrating the truth, or otherwise, of this proposition by logical argument. When studying mathematics at secondary school, pupils are mainly concerned with learning techniques but, in reality, pure mathematics is mainly concerned with proof. Theorems and proofs did not occur to their originators in the 'semi-polished' form which you find in textbooks. The mathematician has an intuitive, instinctive feeling that some proposition may be true. The essence of proof is to establish whether the result is, indeed, true or whether he has been deceived by such a feeling. In this book we discuss various methods of proof which are commonly used in mathematics. Fundamentally, mathematical proof is based on logical argument, that is, to establish from a hypothesis 'p is true' a conclusion 'q is true'.

A problem such as

'Show that $x^2 + 4x + 5$ is positive'

is really of this form if we realise that there is here an unstated hypothesis that x is a real number.

Hypothesis $\qquad\qquad\qquad\qquad p : x \in \mathbb{R}.$

Conclusion $\qquad\qquad\qquad\qquad q : x^2 + 4x + 5 > 0.$

The logical argument in this case would involve

$$x^2 + 4x + 5 = (x + 2)^2 + 1 \geqslant 1 > 0,$$

the reasons for the validity of the various signs between the expressions and the final deduction that $x^2 + 4x + 5 > 0$.

1.2 The place of experiment and diagrams in mathematical proof

We begin with a note of warning. Except for situations in which only a finite number of possibilities need examination, *propositions cannot be proved by experiment*.

Example 1

$$1^3 + 2^3 = \quad 9 = (1 + 2)^2,$$

$$1^3 + 2^3 + 3^3 = \quad 36 = (1 + 2 + 3)^2,$$

$$1^3 + 2^3 + 3^3 + 4^3 = 100 = (1 + 2 + 3 + 4)^2,$$

$$1^3 + 2^3 + 3^3 + 4^3 + 5^3 = 225 = (1 + 2 + 3 + 4 + 5)^2.$$

This pattern *suggests* that the sum of the cubes of the first n natural numbers is equal to the square of their sum, that is to the conjecture that, for $n \in \mathbb{Z}^+$,

$$\sum_{r=1}^{n} r^3 = \left(\sum_{r=1}^{n} r \right)^2. \tag{1.1}$$

Indeed, verification for the further cases $n = 6, 7, \ldots, 20$ would seem to give the result (1.1) still more plausibility but there are infinitely many cases not dealt with, however far we go with our trial process. If we found a case in which the result (1.1) was wrong, of course we would discard the conjecture, but verifying for even 10^{10} special cases will in no way prove (1.1) for all $n \in \mathbb{Z}^+$.

To be completely convinced we must have a *mathematical proof*. (In this case the result can be proved by the method of mathematical induction—see page 40.)

Example 2 If we consider $f(n)$, where $f(n) \equiv n^2 + n + 1$ for $n \in \mathbb{Z}^+$, we find that $f(1) = 3$, $f(2) = 7$, $f(3) = 13$, making us suspect that $f(n)$ is prime for all $n \in \mathbb{Z}^+$. But clearly $f(4) = 16 + 4 + 1 = 21$ and, therefore, $f(4)$ is divisible by 3 and 7. So, despite some evidence from simple experiment, $f(n)$ is not prime for all $n \in \mathbb{Z}^+$. Similarly $n^2 - n + 41$ is prime for $0 \leqslant n \leqslant 40$, $n \in \mathbb{Z}$, but it is $(41)^2$ and, therefore, not prime when $n = 41$.

Note that these examples illustrate the general principle that a single *counter-example* is sufficient to disprove a proposition. By 'counter-example' we mean an example for which the general proposition is not true, i.e. one which runs counter to the general proposition. Thus, 'all boys enjoy games' is immediately disproved by finding one boy who dislikes games.

Finally, caution must be exercised when recourse is made to diagrams. Although diagrams are very useful aids in that they often help us to understand what is going on and, indeed, frequently give us ideas for methods of proof, they can sometimes lead us astray. Even when the diagram is valuable it cannot, of itself, constitute a proof. There follow two examples in which the diagram is valuable and two in which too much reliance on a diagram leads to error.

*Example 3 If $f(x)$ is continuous in the interval $[a, b]$, has a derivative at every point in (a, b) and $f(a) = f(b)$ then there exists at least one point β in (a, b) such that $f'(\beta) = 0$.

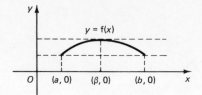
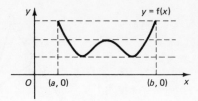

Fig. 1.1   Fig. 1.2

Figures 1.1 and 1.2 illustrate the theorem and strongly suggest its truth. This, however, is not in itself sufficient and the theorem can and should be proved independently of the figure.

Example 4 In this example, which seeks to establish the 'trapezium rule' for the evaluation of an approximate value of a definite integral, Fig. 1.3 is an essential part of the process.

To obtain an approximate value for $\int_a^b f(x)\,dx$, the area A of the region bounded by $y = f(x)$, the x-axis, and the ordinates $x = a$, $x = b$ is divided into strips of equal width h by ordinates P_0N_0, P_1N_1, P_2N_2, ..., P_nN_n of lengths $y_0, y_1, \ldots, y_n$ respectively. Then A is approximately equal to

$$\sum_{r=0}^{n-1} \text{Area }(P_rN_rN_{r+1}P_{r+1}) = \sum_{r=0}^{n-1} \left(\frac{y_r + y_{r+1}}{2}\right)h$$

$$= \frac{1}{2}h\left(y_0 + y_n + 2\sum_{r=1}^{n-1} y_r\right).$$

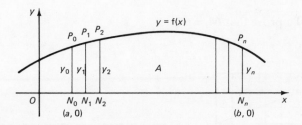

Fig. 1.3

In this method the small parts of the curve P_rP_{r+1} are being approximated to straight lines giving the area as a sum of trapezia.

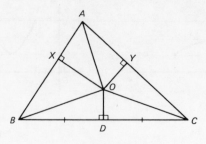

Fig. 1.4

Example 5 To prove that any triangle is equilateral.

Figure 1.4 shows *any* triangle *ABC* in which the internal bisector of angle *BAC* meets the perpendicular bisector of *BC* at *O*. The lines *OX* and *OY* are perpendicular to *AB* and *AC* respectively.

O is equidistant from *AB* and *AC*, as *AO* is the bisector of angle *BAC*. Hence *OX* = *OY*. Also, *O* is equidistant from *B* and *C*, as *OD* is the perpendicular bisector of *BC*. Hence *OB* = *OC*.

In the right-angled triangles *OXB* and *OYC*,

$$\sin \angle OBX = \frac{OX}{OB} = \frac{OY}{OC} = \sin \angle OCY.$$

Hence $\angle OBX = \angle OCY$.

Now from isosceles triangle *OBC*, $\angle OBC = \angle OCB$, and so by adding these two equations $\angle ABC = \angle ACB$. Hence triangle *ABC* is isosceles.

Similarly it can be proved that $\angle BAC = \angle BCA$. Hence triangle *ABC* is equilateral.

It is left to the reader to discover the fallacy which leads to this patent absurdity. (Hint: Fig. 1.4 is a badly drawn diagram; make a really *good* diagram.)

Example 6 To prove that 64 = 65.

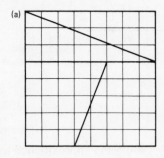
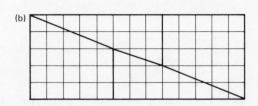

Fig. 1.5

Figures 1.5(a) and (b) show a square and a rectangle each divided into four parts—two triangles and two trapezia which are exactly alike in each. Hence the total area of the four parts is the same in each diagram. But the square is of area 64 square units and the rectangle 65 square units. Hence $64 = 65$.

In this one you need to look very carefully at the diagrams to see where the discrepancy lies.

Example 7 n points lie on a circle C and their joins divide the interior into r_n regions. Find r_n when no three joins are concurrent at an internal point of the circle.

We have $r_1 = 1$, $r_2 = 2$, $r_3 = 4$, $r_4 = 8$, $r_5 = 16$ by drawing a diagram and counting. This might lead us to conjecture that $r_n = 2^{n-1}$. However, $r_6 = 31$. (You can check this by drawing a careful figure.) In fact, it can be proved that

$$r_n = 1 + (n(n-1)(n^2 - 5n + 18)/24).$$

The proof of a result may be easy in some cases and the student is tempted to extrapolate the result to more general cases without an appropriate proof. But sometimes the seemingly easy proof may be quite invalid.

Example 8   It is reasonably straightforward to prove that $2^x \cdot 2^y = 2^{x+y}$ when $x, y \in \mathbb{N}$. But does the formula still hold if $x, y \in \mathbb{R}$? This forces us to consider what we mean by 2^π, say, and we need the definition

$$2^\pi = \exp(\pi \ln 2)$$

and properties of the exponential function before we can proceed.

Example 9   Show that

$$\frac{\mathrm{d}}{\mathrm{d}x} x^n = nx^{n-1}.$$

The argument requires the binomial theorem applied to $(x + h)^n$ which is proved by induction, if $n \in \mathbb{N}$. However, if $n \in \mathbb{R}$, then Taylor's theorem is needed, a far harder result to establish.

Example 10   The Cayley–Hamilton theorem states that an $n \times n$ matrix $\mathbf{A}$ satisfies its own characteristic equation, that is the equation

$$\det(\mathbf{A} - \lambda \mathbf{I}) = 0. \tag{1.2}$$

Putting $\lambda = \mathbf{A}$ appears to give a proof of the theorem at once, and indeed Cayley himself regarded the theorem as self-evident because

$$\det(\mathbf{A} - \mathbf{A}\mathbf{I}) = \det(\mathbf{A} - \mathbf{A}) = \det \mathbf{O} = 0.$$

This method would, however, also seem to imply that $\lambda = \mathbf{A} + \mathbf{B}$, where $\mathbf{B}$ is any singular matrix, also satisfies (1.2), because

$$\det [\mathbf{A} - (\mathbf{A} + \mathbf{B})\mathbf{I}] = \det (\mathbf{A} - \mathbf{A} - \mathbf{B}) = \det (-\mathbf{B}) = 0.$$

But it is not true, in general, that $\mathbf{A} + \mathbf{B}$ satisfies the characteristic equation of $\mathbf{A}$ for any singular $\mathbf{B}$.

The theorem really relates to the expanded form of (1.2), i.e.

$$a_0 + \sum_{i=1}^{n} a_i \lambda^i = 0,$$

which becomes

$$a_0 \mathbf{I} + \sum_{i=1}^{n} a_i \mathbf{A}^i = \mathbf{O}$$

in the theorem.

A proper proof of the theorem is rather more complicated.

2 The notation for implications

2.1 The idea of implication

Suppose p and q are two statements. Then, by p implies q, written symbolically as $p \Rightarrow q$, we mean that, if p is a true statement then q is also a true statement.

Example 1 Suppose p stands for the statement 'x is greater than 2', written as $x > 2$ for short, and q stands for '$x > 1$'. We write

$$p: x > 2,$$

$$q: x > 1.$$

Now any number which is greater than 2 is also greater than 1, so it follows that if p is true then q is true, or

$$p \Rightarrow q.$$

There are several ways in which $p \Rightarrow q$ can be expressed, and it is important to be familiar with those commonly used.

(i) 'if p then q': this is a shortened form of 'if p (is a true statement) then q (is a true statement).

(ii) 'p only if q': this is saying that p can only be true if q is true, as opposed to q being false. In our example a number can only be greater than 2 if it is greater than 1 (as opposed to less than or equal to 1).

(iii) 'p is a sufficient condition for q': this is saying that the truth of p is sufficient to imply the truth of q. If we wish to show $x > 1$, then it is sufficient to show that $x > 2$.

(iv) 'q is a necessary condition for p': this is saying that the truth of q is necessary for p to be true. In our example a number must necessarily be greater than 1 if it is greater than 2.

Notice that in all the above, the statement $p \Rightarrow q$ does not require that p is true or p is false, but only that q is true if p is true.

Notice also the effect of taking different values for x.

$$x = 3, \qquad p \text{ is true}, \qquad q \text{ is true}.$$

$$x = 1\tfrac{1}{2}, \qquad p \text{ is false}, \qquad q \text{ is true}.$$

$$x = 0, \qquad p \text{ is false}, \qquad q \text{ is false}.$$

The implication $p \Rightarrow q$ holds whatever value x has, but the implication says nothing about q if p is false. The only excluded case is p is true and q is false.

One ploy that mathematicians use to prove the falsity of a statement p, is to show that $p \Rightarrow q$ and also that q is false. In other words to show that, if p is true then q is true, and also show that q is false which means, therefore, that p must be false.

Example 2

$p: n^2 + 1$ is an odd number $\forall n \in \mathbb{Z}^+$.

$q: n^2$ is an even number $\forall n \in \mathbb{Z}^+$.

Now $p \Rightarrow q$, since subtracting 1 from an odd number gives an even number. However, 'n^2 is even' is false when n is odd, say $n = 3$, and so q is a false statement. The implication $p \Rightarrow q$ is valid and useful even though it transpires that p and q are false.

A statement p has a *negation*. This is a statement that is false when p is true and is true when p is false. A negation of p can usually be obtained by the insertion of the word 'not' in a suitable position in p. For example 'x is not a prime' is the negation of 'x is a prime'. Symbolically the negation of p is written $\sim p$ and read as 'not p'.

Example 3

$p: n$ is a multiple of 3,

$\sim p: n$ is not a multiple of 3.

Example 4

$p: x > 0$,

$\sim p: x$ is not greater than 0, or, better, $x \leqslant 0$.

Example 5

$p:$ the coplanar lines l and m are parallel,

$\sim p:$ the coplanar lines l and m are not parallel or lines l and m intersect.

Example 6

$p:$ the series $\sum\limits_{r=1}^{\infty} u_r$ is convergent,

$\sim p:$ the series $\sum\limits_{r=1}^{\infty} u_r$ is not convergent.

Example 7

$p:$ the equation $ax^2 + bx + c = 0$ where $a, b, c \in \mathbb{R}$, has two non-real roots,

$\sim p:$ the equation $ax^2 + bx + c = 0$ where $a, b, c \in \mathbb{R}$, has no non-real roots (since non-real roots occur in pairs).

Example 8
$$p: \mathbf{a} \cdot \mathbf{b} = 0,$$
$$\sim p: \mathbf{a} \cdot \mathbf{b} \neq 0.$$

It is important to note that $p \Rightarrow q$ does not mean that $q \Rightarrow p$, that is, the implication sign is unidirectional. This can readily be seen from example 1,

$$p: x > 2,$$

$$q: x > 1.$$

Quite clearly $q \not\Rightarrow p$ as x could, for instance, be equal to $1\frac{1}{2}$ and so q is true but p is false. However, it does follow that $\sim q \Rightarrow \sim p$, in fact the statements $p \Rightarrow q$ and $\sim q \Rightarrow \sim p$ are always equivalent. They are just different ways of expressing the same implication. We write

$$(p \Rightarrow q) \equiv (\sim q \Rightarrow \sim p).$$

Using example 1

$$\sim p: x \leqslant 2,$$

$$\sim q: x \leqslant 1.$$

If $x \leqslant 1$, it certainly follows that $x \leqslant 2$ so that

$$\sim q \Rightarrow \sim p.$$

Students may not realise it but this principle is frequently used in everyday arguments. For instance, a light has been left on overnight and one may hear 'I couldn't have left the light on as I did not go into the room after dark.' Using our terminology

p: person A left a light on overnight in a room,

q: person A used the room after dark,

and accepting $p \Rightarrow q$, then we must accept $\sim q \Rightarrow \sim p$, which person A uses as a defence. In fact, the much-used defence of the 'alibi' is based on this principle.

p: person A broke into B's shop between 1 a.m. and 6 a.m.,

q: person A was at the shop sometime between 1 a.m. and 6 a.m.

Clearly $p \Rightarrow q$.

An alibi consists of proving $\sim q$, hence $\sim q \Rightarrow \sim p$ and so the defence is proved.

Returning to mathematical examples,

Example 9
$$p: a = b,$$
$$q: a^2 = b^2.$$

Clearly $p \Rightarrow q$.
$$q \not\Rightarrow p, \qquad (-2)^2 = 2^2 \quad \text{but} \quad -2 \neq 2.$$
$$\sim q \Rightarrow \sim p, \qquad (a^2 \neq b^2) \Rightarrow (a \neq b).$$

Example 10
p: n is a multiple of 6,
q: n is a multiple of 3.

$p \Rightarrow q$,   any multiple of 6 has a factor 3 and is therefore a multiple of 3.
$q \not\Rightarrow p$,   9 is a multiple of 3 but not a multiple of 6.
$\sim q \Rightarrow \sim p$,   a number which is not a multiple of 3 is not a multiple of 6.

Example 11
p: in the scale of 10 an integer n ends with the digit 5,
q: 5 is a factor of n.

$p \Rightarrow q$.
$q \not\Rightarrow p$ (5 is a factor of 10 but 10 does not end with 5).
$\sim q \Rightarrow \sim p$ (5 is not a factor of n implies that n cannot end in a 5).

The symbol $\Leftarrow$ is also available between two statements and is to be read 'is implied by' so that $p \Rightarrow q$ and $q \Leftarrow p$ are different ways of writing the same statement.

In this chapter we have looked at a number of examples in which $p \Rightarrow q$ but $q \not\Rightarrow p$, but there are, as we shall see, a great number of examples in mathematics in which $p \Rightarrow q$ and $q \Rightarrow p$. That is, the statement $p \Rightarrow q$ and its *converse* $q \Rightarrow p$ are both true. When this is so it is usual to run the two statements together and write $p \Leftrightarrow q$.

Example 12
p: n is an even integer,
q: $(n + 1)$ is an odd integer.

$$p \Rightarrow q, \quad \text{if } n \text{ is even then } n + 1 \text{ is odd.}$$
$$q \Rightarrow p, \quad \text{if } n + 1 \text{ is odd then } n \text{ is even.}$$
Hence $p \Leftrightarrow q$.

We can dispense with the p and q and write the implication between statements directly.

Example 13
(In triangle ABC, $AB = AC$) $\Leftrightarrow$ (In triangle ABC, angle B = angle C).

This is the isosceles triangle theorem and its converse:
Theorem: if two sides of a triangle are equal then the angles opposite those sides are equal.
Converse: if two angles of a triangle are equal then the sides opposite those angles are equal.

Both theorem and converse are true; hence the use of $\Leftrightarrow$.

Example 14   With the usual notation for a triangle

$$(A = \pi/2) \quad \Leftrightarrow \quad (a^2 = b^2 + c^2).$$

The statement $(A = \pi/2) \Rightarrow (a^2 = b^2 + c^2)$ is the theorem of Pythagoras, that is 'If a triangle is right-angled then the square on the hypotenuse is equal to the sum of the squares on the other two sides.'

The statement $(a^2 = b^2 + c^2) \Rightarrow (A = \pi/2)$ is the converse, that is 'If the square on one side of a triangle is equal to the sum of the squares on the other two sides then the triangle is right-angled.'

Both theorem and converse are true, hence the use of $\Leftrightarrow$.

Necessary and sufficient

These words were used at the beginning of this chapter and are very important. We now give a simple example to help to clarify their use.

Example 15
p: n is a multiple of 15,
q: n is a multiple of 5.

Hence $p \Rightarrow q$ but $q \not\Rightarrow p$.

To show that n is a multiple of 5, it is *sufficient* to show that n is a multiple of 15 since any multiple of 15 is certainly a multiple of 5. Thus p is a sufficient condition for q. It is not, however, *necessary* to show that n is a multiple of 15 in order to show that n is a multiple of 5, for instance 10 is not a multiple of 15 but is a multiple of 5. Thus p is not a necessary condition for q.

To show that n is a multiple of 15 it is *necessary* to show that n is a multiple of 5 since any number which is a multiple of 15 must be a multiple of 5. Thus q is a necessary condition for p. It is not, however, *sufficient* to show that n is a multiple of 5 if we wish to show n is a multiple of 15, as only numbers which are multiples of 3 as well as 5 are multiples of 15. Thus q is not a sufficient condition for p.

$$(p \Rightarrow q) \equiv (p \text{ is sufficient for } q)$$

$$\equiv (q \text{ is necessary for } p).$$

Hence when we have $p \Leftrightarrow q$, as in examples 12, 13, 14, then p is a necessary *and* sufficient condition for q.

This is sometimes shortened to

$$p \text{ is true if and only if } q \text{ is true,}$$

or p if and only if q,

or even p iff q.

We adopt a convention that '$p \Rightarrow q \Rightarrow r$' is to be interpreted as '$p \Rightarrow q$' and '$q \Rightarrow r$' with similar meanings to longer sequences and sequences such as '$p \Leftarrow q \Leftarrow r$' and '$p \Leftrightarrow q \Leftrightarrow r$'.

Summary of symbols

$p \Rightarrow q$ if p then q.

$p \Leftrightarrow q$ p if and only if q.

$\sim p$ not p.

$(q \Rightarrow p)$ is the converse of $(p \Rightarrow q)$.

$(\sim q \Rightarrow \sim p)$ is equivalent to $(p \Rightarrow q)$.

The use of these various phrases and symbols is illustrated in the following examples.

Example 16 $x, y \in \mathbb{Z}^+$.

(i) (the product xy is odd) $\Leftrightarrow$ (x is odd and y is odd),

OR   the product xy is odd iff x is odd and y is odd,

OR   for the product xy to be odd, necessary and sufficient conditions are that x is odd and y is odd.

This could be expressed by means of a statement and its converse both of which are true

Statement: If the product xy is odd, then both x and y are odd,

  OR   That x and y are both odd is a necessary condition for xy to be odd.

Converse: If both x and y are odd, then the product xy is odd,

  OR   That x and y are both odd is a sufficient condition for xy to be odd.

(ii) (x and y are both even) $\Rightarrow$ (the product xy is even).

Statement: If x and y are both even, then the product xy is even,

  OR   That x and y are both even is a sufficient condition for xy to be even.

Converse: The converse of this statement is *not* true and a counter-example is provided by $x = 2$, $y = 3$. It is not *necessary* for both x and y to be even in order that xy should be even.

(iii) (the product xy is even) $\Leftrightarrow$ (at least one of x and y is even),

OR   the product xy is even iff at least one of x and y is even,

OR   for the product xy to be even, a necessary and sufficient condition is that at least one of x and y is even.

Write this out as a statement and its converse as in (i).

Example 17

($ABCD$ is a rhombus) $\Leftrightarrow$ (AC and BD bisect each other at right angles),

OR $ABCD$ is a rhombus iff AC and BD bisect each other at right angles,

OR   A necessary and sufficient condition for $ABCD$ to be a rhombus is that AC and BD bisect each other at right angles.

  Statement and converse could be expressed separately as:

Statement: If $ABCD$ is a rhombus, then AC and BD bisect each other at right angles.

Converse: If AC and BD bisect each other at right angles then $ABCD$ is a rhombus.

Rewrite this using the words 'necessary' and 'sufficient'.

Example 18

$(x^2$ is even$) \Leftrightarrow (x$ is even$)$.

Proof of $\Rightarrow$ starting from the left-hand side.

$$(x^2 \text{ is even}) \quad \Rightarrow \quad (x^2 \text{ has a factor 2})$$
$$\Rightarrow \quad (x \text{ has a factor 2})$$
$$\Rightarrow \quad (x \text{ is even}).$$

As explained on page 9, $p \Rightarrow q$ and $\sim q \Rightarrow \sim p$ are equivalent.
Proof of $\Rightarrow$ starting from the negation of the right-hand side.

$$(x \text{ is not even}) \quad \Rightarrow \quad (x = 2k + 1 \text{ for some } k \in \mathbb{Z})$$
$$\Rightarrow \quad [x^2 = 4k(k + 1) + 1]$$
$$\Rightarrow \quad (x^2 \text{ is not even}).$$

Proof of $\Leftarrow$ starting from the right-hand side.

$$(x \text{ is even}) \quad \Rightarrow \quad (x = 2m \text{ for some } m \in \mathbb{Z})$$
$$\Rightarrow \quad (x^2 = 4m^2)$$
$$\Rightarrow \quad (x^2 \text{ is even}).$$

Example 19

$f(x)$ is a polynomial in x.
$[(x - a)$ is a factor of $f(x)] \Leftrightarrow [f(a) = 0]$.

Statement: If $(x - a)$ is a factor of $f(x)$, then $f(a) = 0$,
    OR $f(a) = 0$ is a necessary condition for $(x - a)$ to be a factor of $f(x)$.
Converse: If $f(a) = 0$, then $(x - a)$ is a factor of $f(x)$,
    OR $f(a) = 0$ is a sufficient condition for $(x - a)$ to be a factor of $f(x)$.

Example 20

$f'(x)$ exists for $x \in \mathbb{R}$.
$[f(x)$ has a maximum value when $x = a] \Rightarrow [f'(a) = 0]$,
OR   If $f(x)$ has a maximum value when $x = a$, then $f'(a) = 0$,
OR   A necessary condition for $f(x)$ to have a maximum value when $x = a$ is that $f'(a) = 0$.

The converse is *not* true, as $f'(a) = 0$ is not a *sufficient* condition for $f(x)$ to have a maximum value when $x = a$. A counter-example is provided by $f(x) = x^3$ and $a = 0$.

Example 21

a and **b** are non-zero vectors.

(**a** is perpendicular to **b**) $\Leftrightarrow$ (**a** . **b** = 0),

OR **a** is perpendicular to **b** iff **a** . **b** = 0,

OR **a** . **b** = 0 is a necessary and sufficient condition for **a** to be perpendicular
   to **b**.

Statement: If **a** is perpendicular to **b**, then **a** . **b** = 0,

        OR **a** . **b** = 0 is a necessary condition for **a** to be perpendicular to **b**.

Converse: If **a** . **b** = 0, then **a** is perpendicular to **b**,

        OR **a** . **b** = 0 is a sufficient condition for **a** to be perpendicular to **b**.

Exercise 2.1

1 f(x) is a polynomial.
   $p: (x - a)^2$ is a factor of f(x).
   $q: f'(a) = 0$.
   Place a suitable symbol between p and q and prove your result.

2 P is a sufficient condition for Q.
   If Q then R.
   S is implied by R.
   S is true only if T is true.
   U is necessary for T.
   Does $P \Rightarrow U$?

3 Which of the following is the negation of (P and Q)?
   A $(\sim P)$ or $(\sim Q)$.
   B P or $(\sim Q)$.
   C $(\sim P)$ or Q.
   D $(\sim P)$ and $(\sim Q)$.
   E P or Q.

4 Which one of the following is equivalent to $(P \Rightarrow Q)$?
   A $Q \Rightarrow P$.
   B $(\sim Q) \Rightarrow P$.
   C $Q \Rightarrow (\sim P)$.
   D $(\sim Q) \Rightarrow (\sim P)$.
   E $(\sim P) \Rightarrow (\sim Q)$.

5 $\theta/\pi \in \mathbb{N}$ is
   A a sufficient condition for $\sin \theta = 0$.
   B a necessary condition for $\sin \theta = 0$.
   C a necessary and sufficient condition for $\sin \theta = 0$.
   D a sufficient condition for $\cos \theta = 1$.
   E a necessary condition for $\cos \theta = 1$.

6 $\theta/\pi \in \mathbb{Z}$ is *not*
   A a sufficient condition for $\sin \theta = 0$.
   B a necessary condition for $\sin \theta = 0$.
   C a necessary and sufficient condition for $\sin \theta = 0$.
   D a sufficient condition for $\cos \theta = 1$.
   E a necessary condition for $\cos \theta = 1$.

7 f is a continuous function of x in (a, b).

$p: [f(a) > 0, f(b) < 0]$.

$q: [\exists\ c$ in (a, b) such that $f(c) = 0]$.

Place a suitable symbol between p and q and express your result in words. [$\exists$ means 'there exists'.]

8 $p: y = x^2$.

$q: \dfrac{dy}{dx} = 2x$.

Which one of the following is correct?

A p is a necessary condition for q.
B p is a necessary and sufficient condition for q.
C $(\sim p)$ is a sufficient condition for $(\sim q)$.
D $(\sim q)$ is a necessary condition for $(\sim p)$.
E q is a necessary condition for p.

9 $p: (x - 1)(x - 2) > 0$.

$q: x > 2$.

Which one of the following is *incorrect*?

A $q \Rightarrow p$.
B $(\sim p) \Rightarrow (\sim q)$.
C q is a sufficient condition for p.
D q is a necessary condition for p.
E p is a necessary condition for q.

10 Write down (a) necessary and sufficient condition(s) for the quadrilateral $ABCD$ to be a parallelogram. Express your answer in symbolic form. Is there another possible answer to the question or are such conditions unique?

2.2 Axioms and definitions

As already indicated, scientists carrying out experimental investigations cannot prove a theory by experiment—indeed their physical laws or theories are based on *induction* or *analogy*, that is, inferring the existence of general physical laws from observations or by comparison with similar circumstances.

However, in mathematics we adopt a different outlook. Starting from a set of initial assumptions called *postulates* or *axioms*, we establish, by logical *deductive* reasoning certain propositions or theorems. If the axioms are accepted, then any resulting theorem which is a logical consequence of the axioms must also be accepted. But one mathematician's axioms may be another mathematician's theorems and vice versa. In fact, we can use any set of axioms we choose, provided that they are mutually consistent. However, some sets of axioms are fruitful whereas others are not.

A good example of an axiomatic theory with which most students will be familiar is group theory. Starting only with the primitive concepts of a set and a binary operation relating members of that set, the whole structure is built up on the basis of the axioms of closure, associativity, existence of identity and existence of inverses. These are sufficient to build up a large and widely applicable theory. Commutativity could be required as an extra axiom, and this leads to a further fruitful theory, that of Abelian groups. Dropping the associativity axiom, however, has not led to any great theory. Another axiom system relates to Euclidean geometry. Euclid's original axiom set is not satisfactory, but there are suitable sets containing many more axioms than were needed for group theory (see *A Modern Introduction to Geometry*, A. Tuller, Van Nostrand). The axioms are not provable unless some other axioms are chosen as starting material. However, the axioms for Euclidean geometry express properties that seem entirely reasonable for such a study. Taking these as the starting point, the usual theorems are proved. In a similar manner Newton's Laws of Motion are taken as the basic axioms of classical mechanics.

The axioms will involve some undefined terms, for example, point and line in the Euclidean axioms and set in the group axioms. This is unavoidable. In respect of proving $p \Rightarrow q$, we often have hidden in p some set of axioms. For instance, the axioms of real numbers can be implied in p if p has some mention of a real number in its statement. Our proof of q is simply a completely correct logical argument from our assumed hypothesis p.

As a particular mathematical subject is developed, you may find that certain properties are used for definitions. For example, we define

(i) the sum of two vectors to be given by the addition of components, or equivalently by the parallelogram law,

(ii) the scalar product $\mathbf{a}.\mathbf{b}$ as $|\mathbf{a}||\mathbf{b}|\cos\theta$ or $a_1b_1 + a_2b_2 + a_3b_3$ etc. Similarly, addition of matrices of like order is defined by addition of corresponding elements. Care must be exercised when distinguishing between definition and proof. Do not waste time attempting to prove axioms or defined properties.

As an example of special interest a complex number is defined as an ordered pair of real numbers

$$\mathbb{C} = \{(x,y): x \in \mathbb{R}, y \in \mathbb{R}\}$$

and, as is usual with ordered pairs, we define

$$((x,y) = (x_1,y_1)) \quad \Leftrightarrow \quad (x = x_1, y = y_1). \tag{2.1}$$

Addition and multiplication are defined by

$$(x_1,y_1) + (x_2,y_2) = (x_1 + x_2, y_1 + y_2),$$

$$(x_1,y_1)(x_2,y_2) = (x_1x_2 - y_1y_2, x_1y_2 + x_2y_1),$$

so that

$$(0,1)(0,1) = (-1,0). \tag{2.2}$$

We identify the real number x with $(x,0)$ and write $\mathrm{i} = (0,1)$ so that equation (2.2) can be written $\mathrm{i}^2 = -1$ and the motivation for the notation $x + \mathrm{i}y$ is now apparent

$$x + \mathrm{i}y = (x,0) + (0,1)(y,0) = (x,0) + (0,y) = (x,y).$$

It is, of course, more usual to write (x, y) as $x + iy$ but the bracketed form does indicate that there is nothing unreal or imaginary about complex numbers. They are just as real as real numbers. With the $x + iy$ notation, (2.1) becomes

$$(x + iy = x_1 + iy_1) \quad \Leftrightarrow \quad (x = x_1 \text{ and } y = y_1).$$

In particular, $0 + i0$ is shortened to 0 and so

$$(x + iy = 0) \quad \Leftrightarrow \quad (x = 0 \text{ and } y = 0).$$

2.3 The meaning of arbitrary

It is appropriate here to explain the use of the word *arbitrary* in mathematics. If a property $P(x)$ is true for arbitrary x, we simply mean that it is true for all x in some set, usually $\mathbb{R}$ or $\mathbb{C}$. For example, if $ax = 0$ for arbitrary x we mean that $ax = 0$ for all x in $\mathbb{R}$ if the content implies that real x are under discussion.

As a second example we could say that

$$|z_1 + z_2| \leqslant |z_1| + |z_2|$$

for arbitrary complex numbers z_1 and z_2, meaning simply that

$$(z_1 \in \mathbb{C}, z_2 \in \mathbb{C}) \quad \Rightarrow \quad (|z_1 + z_2| \leqslant |z_1| + |z_2|).$$

Another use is in the familiar words 'arbitrary constant' used in integration.

For example $$\int \cos x \, dx = \sin x + C, \tag{2.3}$$

where C is an arbitrary constant. Here again, C is any real number. The indefinite integral $\int \cos x \, dx$ denotes the set of functions, each of which has the derivative $\cos x$. These are the functions $x \mapsto \sin x + C$ where C denotes any constant. Our equation would be better written

$$\int \cos x \, dx = \{\sin x + C : C \in \mathbb{R}\},$$

but equation (2.3) is the more usual form. So again arbitrary constant simply means any member from $\mathbb{R}$.

To illustrate and extend the idea of arbitrary constants we quote three important examples.

Example 22

$(a_0 + a_1 z + a_2 z^2 + \ldots + a_n z^n = b_0 + b_1 z + b_2 z^2 + \ldots + b_n z^n$ for arbitrary $z \in \mathbb{C}$ where $a_0, a_1, a_2, \ldots, a_n, b_0, b_1, \ldots, b_n$ are constants$) \quad \Leftrightarrow \quad (a_0 = b_0, a_1 = b_1, \ldots, a_n = b_n)$. This is the principle of equating coefficients.

*Example 23

$$\sum_{n=0}^{\infty} a_n z^n \quad \text{converges for } z \in \mathbb{C}.$$

$$\left(\sum_{n=0}^{\infty} a_n z^n = \sum_{n=0}^{\infty} b_n z^n \quad \text{for arbitrary } z \in \mathbb{C} \right) \quad \Leftrightarrow \quad (a_n = b_n \text{ for } n = 0, 1, 2, \dots).$$

This is the Taylor Series equivalent of example 22.

Example 24   If **a**, **b**, and **c** are three linearly independent vectors and

$$\lambda \mathbf{a} + \mu \mathbf{b} + \nu \mathbf{c} = \lambda_1 \mathbf{a} + \mu_1 \mathbf{b} + \nu_1 \mathbf{c},$$

where $\lambda, \mu, \nu, \lambda_1, \mu_1, \nu_1$ are constants, then $\lambda = \lambda_1$, $\mu = \mu_1$, $\nu = \nu_1$.

Miscellaneous exercise 2

1   Prove the following results. Also, rewrite each result using one of the phrases necessary, sufficient, necessary and sufficient, if, only if, iff, where appropriate. In each case, if the converse is true prove it; if not, explain why not, giving counter-examples where possible.

  (i) $(x^2 \text{ is odd}) \Rightarrow (x \text{ is odd})$.
  (ii) $(x = y) \Rightarrow (x^2 = y^2)$.
  *(iii) **A**, **B** are non-singular $n \times n$ matrices.

$$(\mathbf{AB} = \mathbf{B}^{-1}\mathbf{A}^{-1}) \Rightarrow (\mathbf{BA} = \mathbf{A}^{-1}\mathbf{B}^{-1}).$$

  (iv) $(lx + my = 1 \text{ is a tangent to the ellipse } x^2/a^2 + y^2/b^2 = 1) \Rightarrow (a^2 l^2 + b^2 m^2 = 1)$.
  (v) (The equation $x^3 - 3qx + r = 0$, where $q, r \in \mathbb{R}$, has three distinct real roots)
$$\Rightarrow (r^2 < 4q^3).$$
  (vi) (The equation $a \cos \theta + b \sin \theta = c$, where a, b, c are constants, has two real, distinct roots in the interval $[0, 2\pi]$) $\Leftrightarrow (a^2 + b^2 > c^2)$.
  *(vii) $f(x)$ is integrable in $(-1, 1)$.

$$[f(x) \text{ is an even function}] \Rightarrow \int_{-1}^{1} f(x)\,dx = 2 \int_{0}^{1} f(x)\,dx \ .$$

  (viii) $\left[0 < \dfrac{x}{x-1} < 1 \right] \Rightarrow [x < 0]$.

2   Find necessary and sufficient conditions, in terms of a, b, c, where $a \neq 0$, for

$$ax^2 + bx + c > 0, \quad \forall x \in \mathbb{R}.$$

3   Show that the series whose nth term is $\left(\dfrac{2e^x}{1 + e^x} \right)^n$ converges iff $x < 0$.

4   Show that the equation $e^x = mx$, where $m > 0$, has just two real, positive roots iff $m > e$. [*Hint*: show that the minimum value of $e^x - mx$ is $m(1 - \ln m)$.]

*5   Show that the lines of the line-pair $ax^2 + 2hxy + by^2 = 0$, where $h^2 > ab$, are perpendicular if and only if $a + b = 0$.

6   Show that the equation $f(x) = 0$, where $f(x)$ is a polynomial in x, has two equal roots $x = a$ iff $f(a) = 0$ and $f'(a) = 0$.

7   Find the necessary and sufficient condition(s) for the chord joining the points $(at^2, 2at)$ and $(as^2, 2as)$ on the parabola $y^2 = 4ax$ to pass through the focus $(a, 0)$ of the parabola.

3 Types of theorem

3.1 Existence and non-existence theorems

In elementary mathematics we frequently assume the existence of a solution to a specific problem. For example, we assume the fundamental theorem of algebra, first proved by Gauss, that every polynomial equation of degree n (in the complex variable z) with complex coefficients has at least one root $\in \mathbb{C}$. (An extension of this theorem is that the equation has exactly n roots.) Such a theorem, whose proof is beyond the scope of this book, is called an *existence theorem*.

Example 1 **A** is a singular $n \times n$ matrix and **0** is the null $n \times 1$ column vector. Then there exists (symbol $\exists$) an $n \times 1$ non-null column vector **x** such that $\mathbf{Ax} = \mathbf{0}$.

Non-existence theorems are those in which the proof is given of the logical impossibility of some result. For example, it has been proved logically that it is impossible to trisect an arbitrary angle using only a 'ruler and compasses' construction.

Example 2 The diagram, Fig. 3.1, represents three houses H_1, H_2, H_3, which are to be connected to three services (gas, electricity and water) so that none of the pipes or cables cross. We have connected H_1 and H_2 to all three services and H_3 to E and W. There is now no way to connect H_3 to G without crossing another pipe or cable. However the nine connections are made, at least two of them will cross.

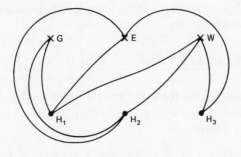

Fig. 3.1

3.2 Uniqueness theorems

In elementary mathematics we frequently assume that the solution, if it exists, to a particular problem is unique. For example, given that

$$\frac{dy}{dx} = f(x, y) \quad \text{and} \quad y = y_0 \text{ when } x = x_0,$$

we assume that, for our particular f, this problem has a unique solution for y in terms of x. [Subject to certain restrictions on $f(x, y)$, this can be proved; but again, this proof is beyond the scope of this book.]

Indeed, behind much of our mathematical work lie assumptions that the solutions obtained are unique. Of course, uniqueness should be proved whenever this is possible.

Example 3 **A** is a non-singular $n \times n$ matrix and **x**, **b** are $n \times 1$ column vectors. Then it can be proved that
 (i) the inverse matrix $\mathbf{A}^{-1}$ is unique,
 (ii) the equation $\mathbf{A}\mathbf{x} = \mathbf{b}$ has a unique solution for **x**.

3.3 Generalisations

Using a simple result we may be able to obtain a much more general result by generalisation. This may require inspired guessing and, probably, but not necessarily, the use of mathematical induction.

Example 4
*(i) $(\cos \theta + i \sin \theta)^2 \equiv \cos 2\theta + i \sin 2\theta$,
 $(\cos \theta + i \sin \theta)^3 \equiv \cos 3\theta + i \sin 3\theta$,
 $(\cos \theta + i \sin \theta)^{-1} = \cos(-\theta) + i \sin(-\theta)$
 suggest $(\cos \theta + i \sin \theta)^n \equiv \cos n\theta + i \sin n\theta$, $n \in \mathbb{Z}^+$ (see page 22).
*(ii) $\mathbf{A}_1, \mathbf{A}_2$ are non-singular $n \times n$ matrices

$$(\mathbf{A}_1 \mathbf{A}_2)^{-1} = \mathbf{A}_2^{-1} \mathbf{A}_1^{-1}$$

suggests $\qquad (\mathbf{A}_1 \mathbf{A}_2 \ldots \mathbf{A}_n)^{-1} = \mathbf{A}_n^{-1} \ldots \mathbf{A}_2^{-1} \mathbf{A}_1^{-1}.$

*(iii) The basis theorem for 3-dimensional real vectors, which states that a set is a basis iff it consists of three linearly independent vectors, can be extended to n-dimensional vectors.

(iv) $\begin{pmatrix} 1 & 0 \\ 0 & 1 \end{pmatrix}$ is the identity 2×2 matrix, and $\begin{pmatrix} 1 & 0 & 0 \\ 0 & 1 & 0 \\ 0 & 0 & 1 \end{pmatrix}$ is the identity 3×3

matrix, suggesting that the $n \times n$ matrix which has all the elements of its leading diagonal equal to 1 and all other elements equal to zero is the identity $n \times n$ matrix.

(v) $\frac{d}{dx}(x) = 1, \frac{d}{dx}(x^2) = 2x, \frac{d}{dx}(x^3) = 3x^2$, leads us to $\frac{d}{dx}(x^n) = nx^{n-1}$, where

$n \in \mathbb{N}$, and to the further generalisation to non-integral values of n, i.e. $n \in \mathbb{R}$.

(vi) Summation of $S_n = 1 + 3 + 5 + \ldots + (2r - 1) + \ldots + (2n - 1)$.
$S_1 = 1$, $S_2 = 4$, $S_3 = 9$, ... suggests $S_n = n^2$.

*(vii) Leibniz's theorem for the differentiation of products dealt with on page 41. [All the examples quoted here are ones in which the generalisation can be proved to be true and, indeed, none of them should be assumed without proof. As was pointed out in chapter 1, there are very real dangers in making general assumptions based on a few special cases so that, however attractive and even obvious the general case appears to be, it should never be assumed without proof.]

Exercise 3

Investigate the truth of the following implications in each of the directions indicated. If any implication is true, prove the result; if false, give a counter-example.

1 $(\overline{x + y}$ is odd$) \Leftrightarrow (xy$ is odd$)$, where $x, y \in \mathbb{Z}^+$.

2 $(x^n = y^n) \Leftrightarrow (x = y)$, where $x, y, n \in \mathbb{Z}^+$.

3 **A** is a 2×2 matrix.
$$(\mathbf{A}^2 = \mathbf{A}) \Leftrightarrow (\text{either } \mathbf{A} = \mathbf{I} \text{ or } \mathbf{A} = \mathbf{O}).$$

4 **A, B** are 2×2 matrices.
$$(\mathbf{A} = \mathbf{O} \text{ or } \mathbf{B} = \mathbf{O}) \Leftrightarrow (\mathbf{AB} = \mathbf{O}).$$

5 (The diagonals of a quadrilateral are perpendicular) $\Leftrightarrow$ (The quadrilateral is a rhombus).

*6 **A, B** are $n \times n$ matrices.
$$(\mathbf{AB} = \mathbf{BA}) \Leftrightarrow [(\mathbf{AB})^\mathrm{T} = \mathbf{A}^\mathrm{T}\mathbf{B}^\mathrm{T}].$$

*7 (Line $lx + my + n = 0$ is a tangent to the ellipse $x^2/a^2 + y^2/b^2 = 1$) $\Leftrightarrow$ $(a^2 l^2 + b^2 m^2 = n^2)$.

8 $f(x)$ is a function of x and a is a constant.
[There is a point of inflexion on the curve $y = f(x)$ at the point where $x = a$] $\Leftrightarrow$ $[f''(a) = 0]$.
[A point of inflexion is a point where the curve crosses its tangent at the point of contact.]

9 $x \in \mathbb{Z}^+ [(x^2 + 2x)$ is a multiple of 3$] \Leftrightarrow [(x^2 - x)$ is a multiple of 3$]$.

**10 (The resultant of a system of coplanar forces is zero) $\Leftrightarrow$ (The system of forces is in equilibrium).

**11 (The speed of a car during a given interval is constant) $\Leftrightarrow$ (The power generated by the engine of the car during that interval is constant).
[Assume constant resistance throughout the interval.]

12 (A ball hits a wall with velocity **u and rebounds with velocity **v**) $\Rightarrow (|\mathbf{v}| < |\mathbf{u}|)$.

13 **P, Q, R are three coplanar forces.
(**P, Q, R** are in equilibrium) $\Leftrightarrow$ (the lines of action of **P, Q, R** are concurrent).

14 $\left(\dfrac{\mathrm{d}^2 x}{\mathrm{d}t^2} = -\omega^2 x\right) \Leftrightarrow (x = a\cos\omega t)$.

15 $(a = b) \Leftrightarrow \left(\displaystyle\int_a^b f(x)\,\mathrm{d}x = 0\right)$.

4 Methods of proof

4.1 Some general observations

Before considering some particular techniques of proof, we first make a few general observations which can assist in understanding proofs.

Generality of conditions

Pure mathematicians usually attempt to establish the truth of a proposition under the least restricting set of conditions possible, so that it will have the widest application possible. However, in many applications the elaborate provisions made by pure mathematicians, to include cases seldom met in practice, are unnecessary and many propositions can be proved more easily under much more restrictive conditions. Indeed, applied mathematicians are usually satisfied by proofs under sufficient (but not necessary) conditions, where the sufficient conditions are the ones they are meeting in practice or are the ones they can easily verify.

For example, de Moivre's theorem is, in many texts, proved for $n \in \mathbb{Q}$, but the proof can be extended to $n \in \mathbb{R}$, thereby including irrational values of n.

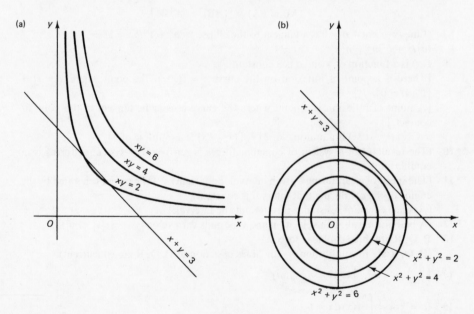

Fig. 4.1

However, if we only wish to use the theorem when $n \in \mathbb{Z}^+$ we might as well just use the simpler proof to establish it under this condition.

Similarly, the binomial theorem for the expansion in ascending powers of x of $(1 + x)^n$ for $n \in \mathbb{Z}^+$ can be proved easily by induction, but the proof for $n \in \mathbb{R}$ requires the use of Taylor's theorem.

Use of figures

Although a diagram is not adequate to prove a proposition, nevertheless it can suggest the truth or otherwise of a proposition and may suggest a 'strategy' of proof. For example, inequalities involving two independent variables are best solved by the use of diagrams as in the following example.

Example 1   Given that $x + y = 3$ and $x, y \geqslant 0$, then the greatest value of xy and the least value of $x^2 + y^2$ both occur when $x = y$. See Figs. 4.1(a) and (b) which suggests the truth of these statements.

A proof can be obtained by substituting $y = 3 - x$ in the expressions xy and $x^2 + y^2$ and completing the square to prove the result.

Example 2   Find $\{x: |x - 2| > 2|x + 1|\}$.
The graphs of $y = |x - 2|$ and $y = 2|x + 1|$ illustrate the relation between these two expressions.

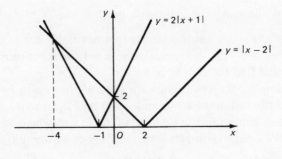

Fig. 4.2

Hence the required set will be $\{x: -4 < x < 0\}$.
A proof can be obtained by saying

$$|x - 2| > 2|x + 1| \quad \Leftrightarrow \quad (x - 2)^2 > 4(x + 1)^2$$

$$\Leftrightarrow \quad x^2 - 4x + 4 > 4x^2 + 8x + 4$$

$$\Leftrightarrow \quad 3x^2 + 12x < 0$$

$$\Leftrightarrow \quad 3x(x + 4) < 0$$

$$\Leftrightarrow \quad -4 < x < 0.$$

Consider all the cases

Consider all the cases

Care must be taken in proofs that all the possible cases are considered. For example, when summing the geometric progression $\sum_{r=1}^{n} x^{r-1}$ the sum when $x \neq 1$ is $(1 - x^n)/(1 - x)$, but this result does not hold, nor is the method of proof valid, when $x = 1$. In this special case, $x = 1$, we substitute $x = 1$ directly into the series and find the sum to be n.

Another example concerns finding the area of the region bounded by the curve $y = f(x)$, the ordinates $x = a$ and $x = b$ and the x-axis, where $f(x)$ is a function which is continuous in the interval (a, b) and which has at most one zero in (a, b). We need to consider separately the cases where $f(a)$ and $f(b)$ are of like sign, in which case the area is simply $\left| \int_{a}^{b} f(x)\,dx \right|$, or of unlike sign in which case the area is $\left| \int_{a}^{c} f(x)\,dx \right| + \left| \int_{c}^{b} f(x)\,dx \right|$ where $f(c) = 0$. This is illustrated in Figs. 4.3(a) and (b).

Example 3 Find $\lim_{n \to \infty} r^n$, where $r \in \mathbb{R}$.

At this stage we assume that
(i) when $r > 1$, $r^n \to \infty$ as $n \to \infty$ (see page 45 for proof).
The various other cases are
(ii) $r = 0$,   (iii) $r = 1$,   (iv) $r = -1$,   (v) $0 < r < 1$,   (vi) $-1 < r < 0$,
(vii) $r < -1$.

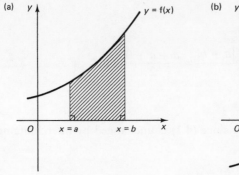

Fig. 4.3

Cases (ii) and (iii) are *trivial* and straightforward and the sequence converges to 0 and 1 respectively.

Case (iv) implies $r^n = (-1)^n$ and the sequence does not converge so that the limit does not exist in this case.

For case (v), put $r = 1/R$ where $R > 1$. Then $r^n = 1/R^n$ and $\lim\limits_{n\to\infty} r^n = \lim\limits_{n\to\infty} 1/R^n$. But, since $R > 1$, by case (i) $R^n \to \infty$ as $n \to \infty$. Thus $\lim\limits_{n\to\infty} 1/R^n = 0$ and so $\lim\limits_{n\to\infty} r^n = 0$. The sequence converges to zero in this case.

For case (vi), put $r = -t$, where $0 < t < 1$. Then $r^n = (-1)^n t^n$ and, by case (v), $\lim_{n\to\infty} r^n = 0$ so that the sequence converges to zero.

For case (vii), put $r = -s$ so that $s > 1$. Then $r^n = (-1)^n s^n$ and since $s > 1$, $s^n \to \infty$ as $n \to \infty$. The sequence, therefore does not converge and the limit does not exist in this case.

Conclusion: As $n \to \infty$ the sequence r^n converges only when $-1 < r \leqslant 1$, converges to zero when $|r| < 1$ and to one when $r = 1$.

Note: In this example we have also illustrated the mathematical technique of using the result for one case to establish the results for other cases.

Example 4 Show that

$$\max(a,b) = \frac{a + b + |a - b|}{2}, \tag{4.1}$$

where $a, b \in \mathbb{R}$.

[Max (a, b) means the greater of a and b.]

Consider the only possible relations between a and b, i.e. $a < b$, $a = b$, $a > b$.

(i) $a < b$.

In this case, $\max(a,b) = b$

and
$$\frac{a + b + |a - b|}{2} = \frac{a + b + b - a}{2} = b,$$

so that (4.1) is correct.

(ii) $a = b$.

In this case, $\max(a, b) = a$

and
$$\frac{a + b + |a - b|}{2} = \frac{a + a + 0}{2} = a.$$

Again (4.1) is correct.

(iii) $a > b$.

In this case we can use symmetry since (4.1) is unchanged by interchanging a and b or

$$\max(a, b) = a$$

$$\frac{a + b + |a - b|}{2} = \frac{a + b + a - b}{2} = a.$$

Thus, in all cases the formula is correct and so holds, in general.

Exercise 4.1 (a)

*1 Find

(i) $\lim\limits_{x \to \infty} \tanh\left(\dfrac{ax + 2}{bx + 1}\right)$,

(ii) $\lim\limits_{x \to 0} \tanh\left(\dfrac{2x + c}{x + d}\right)$.

2 Prove that $\sum\limits_{r=1}^{n} (-1)^r r^2 = n(n + 1)/2$ if n is even,

$$= -n(n + 1)/2 \text{ if } n \text{ is odd}.$$

3 Solve the equations

$$x + ky = a, \quad x + ly = b,$$

and interpret your answers geometrically.

4 Obtain the integral $\displaystyle\int \frac{1}{x^2 + 2ax + b}\, dx$, $a, b \in \mathbb{R}$.

*5 Solve the differential equation

$$\frac{d^2 x}{dt^2} + 2a\frac{dx}{dt} + bx = 0, \quad a, b \in \mathbb{R}.$$

6 Sketch the curves

(i) $y = \dfrac{x}{x^2 + a}$, (ii) $y^2 = \dfrac{x}{x^2 + a}$, $a \in \mathbb{R}$.

7 Show, from first principles, that the distance of the point $P(x_1, y_1)$ from the straight line

$$x \cos\alpha + y \sin\alpha = p, \quad 0 < \alpha < \pi/2 \text{ and } p \in \mathbb{R}^+$$

is equal to

$$\pm(p - x_1 \cos\alpha - y_1 \sin\alpha)$$

according as P is on the origin or non-origin side of the line.

8 Find the number of real roots of the equation
$$x^3 + 3ax + b = 0, \quad a, b \in \mathbb{R}.$$

*9 Solve the equations
$$x + 3y + sz = 4,$$
$$2x - y - 5z = t,$$
$$x + y + 2z = 1,$$

in the cases (a) $s = 9$, $t = -1$, (b) $s = 8$, $t = -1$, (c) $s = 8$, $t = -5/2$, and interpret your answers geometrically.

*10 Investigate the intersection of the three planes with equations
$$x + 2y + 3z = -1,$$
$$x + 6y - z = -5,$$
$$kx + 5z = l.$$

*11 Solve the differential equations

(i) $\dfrac{\mathrm{d}y}{\mathrm{d}x} + ay = \mathrm{e}^{bx}$,

where a, b are constants;

(ii) $\dfrac{\mathrm{d}^2 y}{\mathrm{d}x^2} + n^2 y = \cos px$,

where n and p are constants.

*12 Find conditions under which the integral I exists, where $I = \displaystyle\int_a^b \dfrac{1}{px + q} \, \mathrm{d}x$, $b > a$ and $p \neq 0$. Evaluate I when these conditions are satisfied.

Use of the simplest case

Use of the simplest case

Some propositions can be established under very restrictive conditions and then used to extend the results.

Consider the mean value theorem that, under suitable conditions on a function g,

$$g(b) - g(a) = (b - a)g'(\xi),$$

for some ξ for which $a < \xi < b$. The special case where a function f also satisfies $f(a) = f(b) = 0$ would give

$$0 = f'(\xi),$$

for some ξ for which $a < \xi < b$. This latter, known as Rolle's theorem, is proved first and then the result is applied to $f(x)$ when

$$f(x) = g(b) - g(x) - \frac{(b-x)}{(b-a)}[g(b) - g(a)]$$

to prove the mean value theorem.

Consider next the factor theorem that, if $f(x)$ is a polynomial in x and $(x - a)$ is a factor of $f(x)$, then $f(a) = 0$. This can be extended to give us the remainder theorem, i.e. that the remainder when $f(x)$ is divided by $(x - a)$ is equal to $f(a)$.

In fact, the great mathematician G. Polya suggested 'try the simplest thing first', a hint often worth following.

In some cases assumption of linearity is helpful. For example, in approximating to the real solution of the equation $x^3 + 3x + 1 = 0$, we note that the real root is close to zero and so we neglect x^3 and obtain a first approximation $-1/3$. This intuitively suggests an iterative approach

$$x_{n+1} = -\tfrac{1}{3} - \tfrac{1}{3}x_n^3, \quad x_1 = -\tfrac{1}{3}.$$

However, we need some justification that x_n does tend to the required root.

Exercise 4.1 (b)

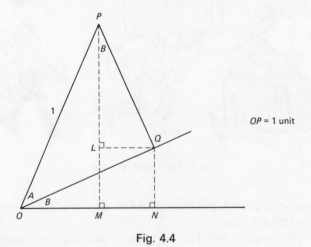

Fig. 4.4

1 Use Fig. 4.4 to prove that $\cos(A + B) = \cos A \cos B - \sin A \sin B$ in the case where $0 < (A + B) < 90°$.

2 Sketch the curve $y = x + x^3$ to indicate its behaviour near the origin.

3 Find the tangent to the curve $y^2 = 4ax$ at the origin.

4 Solve the inequality
$$|x - 2| > 3|x|.$$

5 Write down an equation of a circle on the line joining the points (x_1, y_1) and (x_2, y_2) as diameter. (A diagram suggests the use of the elementary circle property 'an angle in a semicircle is a right angle' to write down this equation immediately.)

6 Find equations of the common tangents to the two circles
$$x^2 + y^2 = 4, \quad x^2 + y^2 - 6x + 8 = 0.$$

7 Write down the coordinates of the fourth vertex of parallelogram $ABCD$, where $A(-1, -1)$, $B(0, 2)$, $C(4, 4)$. (A diagram enables one to see the relationship between the coordinates and so to write down the coordinates of D without further calculation.)

8 Show that the equation $x^3 - 12x + 20 = 0$ has just one real root.

9 Find the area of the region bounded by the curve $y = \sin x$, the x-axis, and the ordinates $x = \pi/3$, $x = k\pi$, where $0 \leqslant k \leqslant 2$.

*10 Solve the differential equation $\dfrac{d^2x}{dt^2} + nx = 0$, where n is a real constant, giving the different cases which arise.

*11 Find the locus of the point representing z in the Argand diagram given that $\left|\dfrac{z - 1}{z - 2}\right| = k$, where $k \in \mathbb{R}^+$.

12 Find the number of real roots of the equation $x^3 - 3x + a = 0$, giving the different cases which arise.

13 Find the set of values of x for which $\dfrac{(x - 1)(x - 2)}{(x + 1)} > 0$.

*14 Use the mean value theorem to prove that, if $h(a) = 0$ and $h'(x) > 0$ for $x > a$, then $h(x) > 0$ for $x > 0$. Use this result to prove that if $f(a) = g(a)$ and $f'(x) > g'(x)$ for $x > a$, then $f(x) > g(x)$ for $x > a$.

Use and extend this result to prove that, for $x > 0$,

(i) $x > \sin x$,

(ii) $\cos x > 1 - x^2/2!$,

(iii) $\sin x > x - x^3/3!$,

(iv) $x - \frac{1}{2}x^2 < \ln(1 + x) < x - \frac{1}{2}x^2 + \frac{1}{3}x^3$,

(v) $x - \frac{1}{3}x^3 + \frac{1}{5}x^5 > \tan^{-1} x > x - \frac{1}{3}x^3$.

[*Hint* for (ii)–(v): $(f'(a) = g'(a), f''(x) > g''(x)$ for $x > a) \Rightarrow (f'(x) > g'(x)$ for $x > a)$.]

4.2 Direct and converse theorems

The direct theorem relates to an implication $P \Rightarrow Q$ and its converse theorem is $P \Leftarrow Q$. In some cases, particularly in coordinate geometry, by judicious use of the symbol $\Leftrightarrow$ it is possible to prove a theorem and its converse together. A string of implications $P \Rightarrow P_1 \Rightarrow P_2 \Rightarrow \ldots \Rightarrow Q$ are used to prove the direct theorem $P \Rightarrow Q$ and, when they are valid, the reverse implications $P \Leftarrow P_1 \Leftarrow P_2 \Leftarrow \ldots \Leftarrow Q$ are used to prove the converse theorem $P \Leftarrow Q$. In writing out these two sequences of implications they are simply combined as $P \Leftrightarrow P_1 \Leftrightarrow P_2 \Leftrightarrow \ldots \Leftrightarrow Q$ and the proofs of $P \Rightarrow Q$ and $P \Leftarrow Q$ are exhibited together.

Example 5 P: The tangents at the points $(at_1{}^2, 2at_1)$ and $(at_2{}^2, 2at_2)$ on the parabola $y^2 = 4ax$ are perpendicular.

Q: The tangents at the points $(at_1{}^2, 2at_1)$ and $(at_2{}^2, 2at_2)$ meet on the directrix $(x = -a)$ of the parabola $y^2 = 4ax$.

Prove that $P \Rightarrow Q$ and its converse $(Q \Rightarrow P)$.

The tangents at $(at_1{}^2, 2at_1)$ and $(at_2{}^2, 2at_2)$ are respectively

$$x - t_1 y + at_1{}^2 = 0,$$
$$x - t_2 y + at_2{}^2 = 0.$$

The x-coordinate of the intersection of these lines is given by $x = at_1 t_2$. Hence

(The tangents are perpendicular) $\Leftrightarrow (t_1 t_2 = -1)$

$\Leftrightarrow$ (the tangents intersect on $x = -a$).

Example 6 Show that the complement $(A \cup B)'$ is equal to the intersection of A' and B'

i.e. $(A \cup B)' = A' \cap B'$.

In effect we must show that any element of the LHS lies in the RHS *and*, conversely, any element of the RHS lies in the LHS, or
$[x \in (A \cup B)'] \Leftrightarrow [x \in A' \cap B']$.

Now $\qquad\qquad [x \in (A \cup B)'] \quad \Leftrightarrow \quad (x \notin A \cup B)$

$\Leftrightarrow \quad (x \notin A \text{ and } x \notin B)$

$\Leftrightarrow \quad (x \in A' \text{ and } x \in B')$

$\Leftrightarrow \quad (x \in A' \cap B')$.

In the one direction we get $\quad (x \in (A \cup B)') \Rightarrow (x \in A' \cap B')$,
which means that $\qquad\qquad (A \cup B)' \subseteq A' \cap B'$. $\qquad\qquad$ (4.2)
In the other direction we get $\quad (x \in (A \cup B)') \Leftarrow (x \in A' \cap B')$
which means that $\qquad\qquad (A \cup B)' \supseteq A' \cap B'$. $\qquad\qquad$ (4.3)
Putting (4.2) and (4.3) together gives the required equality.

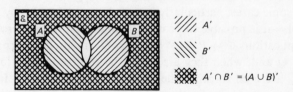

Fig. 4.5

This result has been logically established but is clearly illustrated by reference to a Venn diagram, Fig. 4.5.

Example 7   Show that $[(x - a)$ is a factor of the polynomial $f(x)] \Leftrightarrow [f(a) = 0]$.

By division we have

$$f(x) = (x - a)Q(x) + R,$$

where $Q(x)$ is a polynomial and R is a constant.

Thus $\qquad [(x - a)$ is a factor of $f] \Leftrightarrow (R = 0) \Leftrightarrow [f(a) = 0]$.

4.3   Direct proof

Of course, many results can be proved directly (by substitution for example). By assuming the given data *and these only* many propositions can be established directly.

Example 8   Given that $y = e^{kx}(a \cos nx + b \sin nx)$, where a, b, k and n are constants,

show that $\qquad \dfrac{d^2 y}{dx^2} - 2k \dfrac{dy}{dx} + (n^2 + k^2)y = 0$.

Proof $\qquad [ye^{-kx} = a \cos nx + b \sin nx]$

$$\Rightarrow \left[\frac{d^2}{dx^2}(ye^{-kx}) = -n^2(a \cos nx + b \sin nx) \right]$$

$$\Rightarrow \left[\frac{d^2}{dx^2}(ye^{-kx}) = -n^2 ye^{-kx} \right]$$

$$\Rightarrow \left[\left(\frac{d^2 y}{dx^2} - 2k \frac{dy}{dx} + k^2 y \right) e^{-kx} = -n^2 ye^{-kx} \right].$$

Cancellation of e^{-kx} ($\neq 0$, watch this point) and rearrangement gives the required result.

Example 9   Given that $x = \cos t$, $y = \cos 2pt$, where p is constant, show that

$$(1 - x^2)\frac{d^2 y}{dx^2} - x \frac{dy}{dx} + 4p^2 y = 0.$$

Proof

$$\left[\frac{dy}{dx} = \frac{\dot{y}}{\dot{x}} = \frac{-2p \sin 2pt}{-\sin t} = \pm \frac{2p\sqrt{(1 - y^2)}}{\sqrt{(1 - x^2)}} \right]$$

$$\Rightarrow \left[(1 - x^2) \left(\frac{dy}{dx} \right)^2 = 4p^2(1 - y^2) \right].$$

Differentiation with respect to x and cancellation of $\dfrac{dy}{dx}$ (in general non-zero) gives the required result.

Note: In both examples 8 and 9 we have obtained our conclusion by direct argument from the hypotheses.

Direct proofs can usually be given when dealing with equalities. The strategy required to prove that $A = B$ can vary from problem to problem. For example you can prove $A = B$ by such methods as:

(i) $(A = C$ and $B = C) \Rightarrow (A = B)$.

(ii) $(A - B = 0) \Rightarrow (A = B)$.

(iii) $(A \geqslant B$ and $A \leqslant B) \Rightarrow (A = B)$.

See, however, chapter 6 (page 68) where some common errors are pointed out.

Similarly, when dealing with the inequalities $f(x) > g(x)$ it is usually best to try to establish that $f(x) - g(x) > 0$. (Proving that an expression is positive is usually easier than proving that one expression exceeds another.) Care is needed in getting into the form $f(x) - g(x) > 0$ if this involves multiplying by functions of x.

Example 10 Find the set of values of x for which $\dfrac{x^2 - 3}{x} > 2$.

$$\left[\frac{x^2 - 3}{x} > 2 \right]$$

$$\Leftrightarrow \left[\frac{x^2 - 3}{x} - 2 > 0 \right]$$

$$\Leftrightarrow \left[\frac{x^2 - 2x - 3}{x} > 0 \right]$$

$$\Leftrightarrow \left[\frac{(x - 3)(x + 1)}{x} > 0 \right]$$

$$\Leftrightarrow [x > 3 \quad \text{or} \quad -1 < x < 0].$$

If, however, we wish to multiply the given inequality by x and express it as $x^2 - 2x - 3 > 0$, we must consider the sign of x as follows.

$$\left(\frac{x^2 - 3}{x} > 2, x > 0 \right) \Leftrightarrow (x^2 - 2x - 3 > 0, x > 0)$$

$$\Leftrightarrow [(x - 3)(x + 1) > 0, x > 0]$$

$$\Leftrightarrow (x > 3).$$

$$\left(\frac{x^2 - 3}{x} > 2, x < 0 \right) \Leftrightarrow (x^2 - 2x - 3 < 0, x < 0)$$

$$\Leftrightarrow (-1 < x < 0).$$

Hence $x \in \{x : x > 3$ or $-1 < x < 0\}$ and the solution set is $\{x : -1 < x < 0\} \cup \{x : x > 3\}$. It is, however, much better to multiply the given inequality by x^2 which is positive unless $x = 0$. Thus:

$$\left(\frac{x^2 - 3}{x} > 2\right) \quad \Leftrightarrow \quad [x(x^2 - 3) > 2x^2]$$

$$\Leftrightarrow \quad [x(x^2 - 2x - 3) > 0]$$

$$\Leftrightarrow \quad [x(x - 3)(x + 1) > 0]$$

$$\Leftrightarrow \quad (x > 3 \text{ or } -1 < x < 0).$$

Thus multiplying by x^2 covers all cases. Note that the implications are needed in both directions. The direct implications ($\Rightarrow$) give

$$\left(\frac{x^2 - 3}{x} > 2\right) \Rightarrow (x > 3 \text{ or } -1 < x < 0).$$

This means that

$$\left\{x: \frac{x^2 - 3}{x} > 2\right\} \subseteq \{x: x > 3 \text{ or } -1 < x < 0\}.$$

The reverse implications ($\Leftarrow$) give

$$\left(\frac{x^2 - 3}{x} > 2\right) \Leftarrow (x > 3 \text{ or } -1 < x < 0).$$

This means that

$$\left\{x: \frac{x^2 - 3}{x} > 2\right\} \supseteq (x: x > 3 \text{ or } -1 < x < 0)$$

which is also required by the question since we want

$$\left\{x: \frac{x^2 - 3}{x} > 2\right\} = \{x: x > 3 \text{ or } -1 < x < 0\}.$$

Propositions in coordinate geometry can usually be established directly but do not usually require excessive algebraic manipulation. Some thought may show that techniques from other branches of mathematics, such as calculus, the symmetric functions of the roots of algebraic equations, general symmetry properties of curves, odd and even functions, may simplify proofs.

Example 11 Show that one, two or three normals can be drawn through the point (h, k) to the parabola $y^2 = 4ax$.

The normal at the point $(at^2, 2at)$ has equation $y + tx = at(2 + t^2)$.
The condition for this normal to pass through the point (h, k) is

$$at^3 + (2a - h)t - k = 0.$$

This cubic equation in t has one, two or three (distinct) real roots and so there are either one, two or three normals corresponding to these values of t.

Example 12 Prove that, if $a > 0$, the equation $f(x) = 0$, where $f(x) \equiv x^3 + ax + b$, has only one real root.

The derivative $f'(x)$ is given by

$$f'(x) = 3x^2 + a$$

and, since $a > 0$, we have, for all $x \in \mathbb{R}$, $f'(x) > 0$.

Thus f is increasing and so can only take the value 0 at most once. Moreover, $f(x) \to -\infty$ as $x \to -\infty$ and $f(x) \to +\infty$ as $x \to +\infty$ so that f must take the value 0 for some x. The graph of $f(x)$ in this case is illustrated in Fig. 4.6(a). Note that $a > 0$ is *a sufficient condition* for there to be just one real root but it is *not a necessary* one. The graph could be of the form shown in Fig. 4.6(b) if $a < 0$, i.e. with a maximum and a minimum and still the equation $f(x) = 0$ has only one real root.

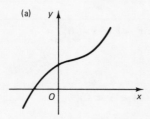 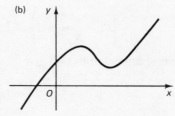

Fig. 4.6

Example 13 Normals are drawn at the points $(ct_1, c/t_1)$, $(ct_2, c/t_2)$, $(ct_3, c/t_3)$, $(ct_4, c/t_4)$ to the rectangular hyperbola $xy = c^2$. Prove that, if the four normals are concurrent, then $t_1 t_2 t_3 t_4 = -1$.

The normal at the point $(ct, c/t)$ is

$$tx - y/t = c(t^2 - 1/t^2).$$

The condition for this normal to pass through a fixed point (h, k) is

$$th - k/t = c(t^2 - 1/t^2),$$

$$\text{i.e.} \quad ct^4 - ht^3 + kt - c = 0.$$

Hence, if each of the given normals passes through (h, k), then t_1, t_2, t_3, t_4 are the roots of this equation and so, using the symmetric functions of the roots

$$t_1 t_2 t_3 t_4 = -1.$$

Note, however, that this is *not* a sufficient condition for the normals to be concurrent.

Exercise 4.3

1 Answer the following questions in the manner of examples 8 and 9 on page 31.

    (i) If $y^n = x + \sqrt{(1 + x^2)}$, prove that $n\sqrt{(1 + x^2)}\dfrac{\mathrm{d}y}{\mathrm{d}x} = y$.

    (ii) If $y = \sin(a \sin^{-1} x)$, prove that

$$(1 - x^2)\frac{\mathrm{d}^2 y}{\mathrm{d}x^2} - x\frac{\mathrm{d}y}{\mathrm{d}x} + a^2 y = 0.$$

(iii) If $y = [x + \sqrt{(1 + x^2)}]^p$, show that

$$(1 + x^2)\frac{\mathrm{d}^2 y}{\mathrm{d}x^2} + x\frac{\mathrm{d}y}{\mathrm{d}x} - p^2 y = 0.$$

(iv) If y is a function of x and $x = \mathrm{e}^t/(\mathrm{e}^t + 1)$, prove that

$$x(1 - x)\frac{\mathrm{d}y}{\mathrm{d}x} = \frac{\mathrm{d}y}{\mathrm{d}t}.$$

(v) If $y = t^m + t^{-m}$ and $x = t + t^{-1}$, prove that

$$(x^2 - 4)\left(\frac{\mathrm{d}y}{\mathrm{d}x}\right)^2 = m^2(y^2 - 4),$$

$$(x^2 - 4)\frac{\mathrm{d}^2 y}{\mathrm{d}x^2} + x\frac{\mathrm{d}y}{\mathrm{d}x} - m^2 y = 0.$$

2 Find the set of real values of x for which

$$\frac{x^2 + 1}{x} > 2.$$

3 Find the set of real values of x for which

$$\frac{x^2 + 2x}{x - 1} > x.$$

4 Find the set of real values of x for which

$$(x - 3)^4 < 16.$$

[In this example it is easier to obtain values for $x - 3$ and then x rather than to try $f(x) - g(x) < 0$.]

4.4 Proof by exhaustion

When only a finite number of possibilities need to be examined, then the method of exhaustion (not to be confused with Archimedes' method of exhaustion), which consists of writing down all the possibilities, can sometimes be used to advantage. Indeed, this may be the only possible method of proof.

Example 14 Prove that $n^3 - n$, where $n \in \mathbb{Z}^+$, is a multiple of 6.
Proof: In arithmetic modulo 6, the only numbers are 0, 1, 2, 3, 4, 5. But

$$0^3 \equiv 0 \pmod 6,$$

$$1^3 \equiv 1 \pmod 6,$$

$$2^3 \equiv 2 \pmod 6,$$

$$3^3 \equiv 3 \pmod 6,$$

$$4^3 \equiv 4 \pmod 6,$$

$$5^3 \equiv 5 \pmod 6.$$

(This is equivalent to considering the six cases $n = 6k$, $n = 6k + 1$, $n = 6k + 2$, $n = 6k + 3$, $n = 6k + 4$, $n = 6k + 5$.) Hence the result follows. (It could also be proved by mathematical induction or by using the fact that any three consecutive positive integers must contain a multiple of 2 and a multiple of 3.)

The method of exhaustion is particularly useful in some branches of algebra, such as the theory of groups.

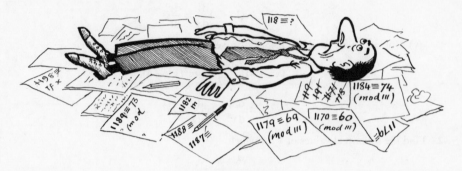

Proof by exhaustion

Exercise 4.4

In questions 1, 2, 3 use the method of exhaustion to establish the given results.
1 There is no solution of $x^2 \equiv 3 \pmod{5}$.
2 There is no solution in integers of the equation $x^2 + y^2 = 19$.
3 The set S, where $S = (0, 1, 2, 3, 4,)$, under addition mod 5 forms a group.
4 Find an integer n such that the real root of the equation

$$x^3 + 7x - 129 = 0$$

lies between n and $n + 1$.

4.5 Transformation to another problem

A basic technique of mathematics is the transformation of a given problem into an equivalent problem (see examples 15–18 below). Even more fundamental is the fact that mathematics consists essentially of transforming problems that we cannot solve at sight into those for which we can *write down* the answer. For example, most problems in theoretical mechanics are eventually changed into

Transformation to another problem

problems of pure mathematics. Examples 15–18 illustrate this technique which you have been using (subconsciously) for a long time.

Example 15

(i) $\displaystyle\int xe^{-2x}\,dx = -\frac{1}{2}\int x\frac{d}{dx}(e^{-2x})\,dx$

$\displaystyle\qquad = -\frac{1}{2}xe^{-2x} + \frac{1}{2}\int e^{-2x}\,dx$

$\displaystyle\qquad = -\frac{1}{4}(2x+1)e^{-2x} + C.$

Here we have transformed the integral from one we cannot recognise at sight, $\int xe^{-2x}\,dx$, into an expression involving $\int e^{-2x}\,dx$, which we can write down.

(ii) Evaluate I, where $I = \displaystyle\int_0^a \sqrt{(a^2 - x^2)}\,dx,\ a > 0.$
The substitution $x = a\sin\theta$ gives

$$I = a^2 \int_0^{\pi/2} \cos^2\theta\,d\theta$$

$$= \frac{1}{2}a^2 \int_0^{\pi/2} (1 + \cos 2\theta)\,d\theta$$

$$= \frac{1}{2}a^2 \left[\theta + \frac{1}{2}\sin 2\theta\right]_0^{\pi/2} = \pi a^2/2.$$

Here, we have transformed the problem twice, once by using integration by substitution and once to express the integrand in a suitable form.

Example 16 Find the set X of values of x for which

$$\left|\frac{x}{x-1}\right| \leqslant 1.$$

$$\left[\left|\frac{x}{x-1}\right| \leqslant 1\right] \Leftrightarrow \left[\left(\frac{x}{x-1}\right)^2 \leqslant 1\right] \qquad (4.4)$$

$$\Leftrightarrow \left[\frac{x^2}{(x-1)^2} - 1 \leqslant 0\right]$$

$$\Leftrightarrow \left[\frac{x^2 - (x-1)^2}{(x-1)^2} \leqslant 0\right]$$

$$\Leftrightarrow \left[\frac{(2x-1)}{(x-1)^2} \leqslant 0\right]$$

$$\Leftrightarrow \left[x \leqslant \frac{1}{2}\right].$$

Thus $$X = \{x : x \leqslant \tfrac{1}{2}\}.$$

Note how we have transformed the inequality into one of the form $f(x) \leqslant 0$, where $f(x)$ is in factor form. This makes it easy for us to *see* the changes in sign of $f(x)$ as x varies.

Alternatively we could multiply the right-hand side of equation (4.4) by $(x - 1)^2$ and obtain

$$[x^2 \leqslant (x - 1)^2] \quad \Leftrightarrow \quad [0 \leqslant -2x + 1]$$

$$\Leftrightarrow \quad (x \leqslant \tfrac{1}{2}).$$

Example 17 An examination consists of five papers, each marked from 0 to 100 marks. In how many ways can a candidate score exactly 200 marks when the totals for his five papers are added together?

There is no simple way in which the problem can be tackled directly, but consider the coefficient of x^n in the expansion of

$$(x^0 + x^1 + x^2 + \ldots + x^{100})^5.$$

Each term contributing to this coefficient is obtained by adding five of the indices 0, 1, 2, ..., 100, where the indices may be repeated. Therefore the coefficient of x^n in this expansion is the number of ways in which five of the marks can be added to total n. In our case we need the coefficient of x^{200} in the expansion of

$$(1 + x + x^2 + \ldots + x^{100})^5, \quad \text{i.e. in } (1 - x^{101})^5/(1 - x)^5.$$

(Note that we have transformed the problem to one involving the binomial series.) Hence, the number of ways is

[the coefficient of x^{200} in the expansion of $(1 - x)^{-5}$]
  $- 5$[the coefficient of x^{99} in the expansion of $(1 - x)^{-5}$]

$$= \frac{201 \cdot 202 \cdot 203 \cdot 204}{4!} - \frac{5 \cdot 100 \cdot 101 \cdot 102 \cdot 103}{4!}$$

$$= 70\,058\,751 - 22\,106\,375$$

$$= 47\,952\,376.$$

Example 18 Given that $x, y \in \mathbb{R}$ and $x^2 + y^2 \leqslant 1$, $x \geqslant 0$, find the greatest and least values of (i) $(x + y)$, (ii) $(x + y)^2$, (iii) $x(x^2 + y^2 - 1)$.

Here we use a geometrical technique. (A formal analytic argument would be rather more involved.)

All points (x, y) for which the given inequalities are satisfied lie in or on the boundary of the semicircular region T (shown shaded) in Fig. 4.7.

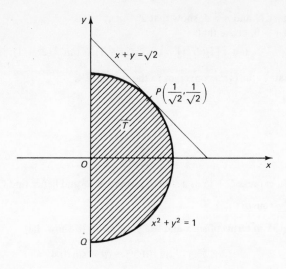

Fig. 4.7

(i) The greatest value of $x + y$ occurs when the line $x + y = $ constant is tangential to the semicircular arc at P (can you see why this is so?), and so has the value $\sqrt{2}$. The least value of $x + y$ is -1 (at Q).

(ii) Therefore the greatest value of $(x + y)^2$ is 2. Also, since the line $x + y = 0$ intersects the region T, the least value of $(x + y)^2$ is zero. (Remember the square of a real number cannot be negative.)

(iii) Let us transform to polar coordinates so that $x = r \cos \theta$, $y = r \sin \theta$, $0 \leqslant r \leqslant 1$, $-\pi/2 \leqslant \theta \leqslant \pi/2$.

Then we have to find the greatest and least values of

$$r(r^2 - 1) \cos \theta.$$

For $0 \leqslant r \leqslant 1$, the greatest and least values of $r(r^2 - 1)$ are 0 and $-2/(3\sqrt{3})$ respectively. (The least value is found by calculus as the minimum when $r = 1/\sqrt{3}$.) Also the greatest and least values of $\cos \theta$ are 1 and 0 respectively. It follows that the greatest and least values of $x(x^2 + y^2 - 1)$ for $(x, y) \in T$ are 0 and $-2/(3\sqrt{3})$ respectively.

Exercise 4.5

*1 By transformation to polar coordinates sketch the curves whose equations are
   (i) $x^2 + y^2 = 4xy$,
   (ii) $(x^2 + y^2)^2 = a^2 x^2$, $a > 0$,
   (iii) $(x^2 + y^2)^2 = a(x^3 - 3xy^2)$, $a > 0$.
2 Show that $xe^{-x} \leqslant 1$ for $x \in \mathbb{R}$.
3 Transform the differential equation given to a separable form by the substitution $y = vx$ and hence solve it:

$$\frac{dy}{dx} = \frac{x + y}{x - y}.$$

4 Given that $n \in \mathbb{N}$ and $n > 4$, show that $2^n > n^2$.

*5 Given that $r > 0$, prove that

$$\tan^{-1}\left[1/(2r^2)\right] = \tan^{-1}(2r+1) - \tan^{-1}(2r-1).$$

Deduce that $\displaystyle\sum_{r=1}^{\infty} \tan\left(\tfrac{1}{2}r^2\right)$ converges to the sum of $\pi/4$.

*6 Given that

$$C = \sum_{r=1}^{n} \cos r\theta,$$

$$S = \sum_{r=1}^{n} \sin r\theta,$$

where $\theta \in \mathbb{R}$, express $C + iS$ as a sum of powers of $e^{i\theta}$ and hence find C. By differentiation find $\displaystyle\sum_{r=1}^{n} r \sin r\theta$.

*7 Express $\sin 3x$ in terms of $\sin x$ and use your result to show that

$$\sum_{r=1}^{\infty} 3^{r-1} \sin^3 (\theta/3^r) = (\theta - \sin \theta)/4.$$

*8 Find the number of different products which can arise (not the sum of their coefficients) when we expand $(a + b + c + d)^{10}$ by verifying that this is the same as the number of ways of arranging ten stars and three crosses in order.

4.6 Mathematical induction

Almost all scientific advances are based on *induction*, which the dictionary defines as 'the inference of a general law from knowledge of particular instances'. The inference is frequently based on intuitive inspiration or guessing. But this must not be confused with *mathematical induction* which is a property of $\mathbb{Z}^+$. The technique is as follows.

Suppose we have to prove a statement P_n, which we suspect is true, for all integers n greater than or equal to an integer k. Then the steps in the proof are:

(i) Prove that the proposition is true for the least value of n, in our case k, i.e. prove that P_k is true.

(ii) Assume P_s is true and, using this assumption, prove that P_{s+1} is true, i.e. prove $P_s \Rightarrow P_{s+1}$ for every integer $s(s \geqslant k)$.

(iii) It follows by the principle of mathematical induction that P_n is true for $n \geqslant k$.

Note: If a theorem has to be established for $n \in \mathbb{Z}^+$, only the special case $k = 1$ is required in (i) above.

The principle of mathematical induction is

$$(P_k, P_s \Rightarrow P_{s+1} \text{ for } s \in \mathbb{N}, s \geqslant k) \quad \Rightarrow \quad (P_s \text{ for all } s \in \mathbb{Z}^+, s \geqslant k).$$

Here we give some illustrative examples, including an important mathematical theorem.

Example 19 Given that the elements of the sequence $\{u_n\}$ satisfy

$$u_{n+1} - 3u_n = 3^n, \quad u_1 = 1,$$

prove that

$$u_n = n3^{n-1}, \quad n \in \mathbb{Z}^+.$$

Our induction hypothesis or statement we wish to prove is

$$P_n : (u_n = n3^{n-1}), \quad n \in \mathbb{Z}^+.$$

(i) P_1 is true since $u_1 = 1 = 1 \cdot 3^0 = 1 \cdot 3^{1-1}$.
(ii) $(u_s = s3^{s-1}) \implies [u_{s+1} = 3u_s + 3^s = 3s3^{s-1} + 3^s = (s+1)3^s]$

or $\qquad P_s \implies P_{s+1}(s \in \mathbb{Z}^+).$

It follows by the principle of mathematical induction that the result is true $\forall n \in \mathbb{Z}^+$.

Example 20   Given that $n \in \mathbb{N}$ prove that f(n), where f$(n) \equiv 3^{4n+2} + 2^{6n+3}$, is divisible by 17.

Our induction hypothesis is $P_n : [17$ divides f$(n)] \, n \in \mathbb{N}$.
(i) Now f$(0) = 3^2 + 2^3 = 9 + 8 = 17$ and so f(0) is divisible by 17, i.e. P_0 is true.
(ii) $\qquad [f(s+1) = 3^{4s+6} + 2^{6s+9} = 81 \times 3^{4s+2} + 64 \times 2^{6s+3}]$

$$\implies [f(s+1) = 64 \times f(s) + 17 \times 3^{4s+2}]$$

Hence $(P_s \implies P_{s+1}) \, s \in \mathbb{N}$.

It follows by the principle of mathematical induction that f(n) is divisible by 17 $\forall n \in \mathbb{N}$.

Example 21   *Leibniz's theorem* for repeated differentiation of a product. Given that u and v are functions of x and $\dfrac{d^r u}{dx^r}, \dfrac{d^s v}{dx^s}$ are denoted by u_r, v_s respectively, then prove

$$P_n : \frac{d^n}{dx^n}(uv) = u_0 v_n + \binom{n}{1} u_1 v_{n-1} + \binom{n}{2} u_2 v_{n-2} + \ldots + \binom{n}{r} u_r v_{n-r}$$

$$+ \ldots + u_n v_0.$$

Proof:
(i) P_1 is simply the product rule for differentiation.
(ii) Assume that the theorem is true for $n = k$.
    Then differentiating (using the product formula)

$$\frac{d^{k+1}}{dx^{k+1}}(uv) = (u_0 v_{k+1} + u_1 v_k) + \binom{k}{1}(u_1 v_k + u_2 v_{k-1}) + \ldots$$

$$+ \binom{k}{r}(u_r v_{k+1-r} + u_{r+1} v_{k-r}) + \ldots + (u_k v_1 + u_{k+1} v_0).$$

The coefficient of the term involving $u_r v_{k+1-r}$ is

$$\binom{k}{r-1} + \binom{k}{r} = \frac{k!}{(r-1)!(k+1-r)!} + \frac{k!}{r!(k-r)!}$$

$$= \frac{(k+1)!}{r!(k+1-r)!}$$

$$= \binom{k+1}{r} \quad \text{for } r = 1, 2, \ldots, k.$$

Hence

$$\frac{d^{k+1}}{dx^{k+1}}(uv) = u_0 v_{k+1} + \binom{k+1}{1} u_1 v_k + \binom{k+1}{2} u_2 v_{k-1} + \cdots$$

$$+ \binom{k+1}{r} u_r v_{k+1-r} + \cdots + u_{k+1} v_0.$$

This is merely the statement of the theorem with $k+1$ in place of k.
Thus $P_k \Rightarrow P_{k+1}$. Hence by mathematical induction the theorem is true for $n \in \mathbb{Z}^+$.

Example 22 Show that

$$\frac{d^n}{dx^n}(xy) = xy_n + ny_{n-1}, \quad \text{where } y_n = \frac{d^n y}{dx^n}. \tag{4.5}$$

By taking $y = x^{n-1} e^{1/x}$, show that

$$P_n : \frac{d^n}{dx^n}(x^{n-1} e^{1/x}) = (-1)^n \frac{e^{1/x}}{x^{n+1}}.$$

The first result comes directly from Leibniz's theorem with $u = x$, $v = y$, or it can be established directly by induction.

We prove P_n by induction.

(i) For P_1:

$$\frac{d}{dx}(x^0 e^{1/x}) = \frac{-e^{1/x}}{x^2} = \frac{(-1)^1 e^{1/x}}{x^{1+1}}$$

and so P_1 is true.

(ii) Assume P_k and consider

$$\frac{d^{k+1}}{dx^{k+1}}(x^k e^{1/x}) = \frac{d^{k+1}}{dx^{k+1}}(x \cdot x^{k-1} e^{1/x}).$$

(Note that we have replaced n by $k+1$ throughout, i.e. in the expression to be differentiated *as well as* in the order of differentiation.)

Using result (4.5) we have

$$\frac{d^{k+1}}{dx^{k+1}}(x^k e^{1/x}) = x \frac{d^{k+1}}{dx^{k+1}}(x^{k-1} e^{1/x}) + (k+1) \frac{d^k(x^{k-1} e^{1/x})}{dx^k}$$

$$= x \frac{d}{dx}\left[\frac{(-1)^k e^{1/x}}{x^{k+1}}\right] + (k+1) \frac{(-1)^k e^{1/x}}{x^{k+1}}$$

$$= \frac{(-1)^{k+1}e^{1/x}}{x^{k+2}} - \frac{(k+1)(-1)^k e^{1/x}}{x^{k+1}} + \frac{(k+1)(-1)^k e^{1/x}}{x^{k+1}}$$

$$= \frac{(-1)^{k+1}e^{1/x}}{x^{(k+1)+1}}.$$

Hence $P_k \Rightarrow P_{k+1}$.

Hence by the principle of mathematical induction P_n is true $\forall n \in \mathbb{Z}^+$.

*$Example\ 23$ Given that $u_1 = 3$, $u_2 = 5$ and $u_{n+2} - 3u_{n+1} + 2u_n = 0$, show that $u_n = 2^n + 1$ for $n \in \mathbb{Z}^+$.

The proof follows a similar line to example 19, except that we must assume P_s and P_{s+1} are both true and hence show that P_{s+2} is true. Prove independently that P_1 and P_2 are true and the result follows by mathematical induction. Here we have used a different form of the principle
i.e. if (i) $P_1, P_2,$
  (ii) $(P_1, P_2, \ldots, P_n) \Rightarrow (P_{n+1})$ $\forall n \in \mathbb{Z}^+,$
then P_n $\forall n \in \mathbb{Z}^+$.

Exercise 4.6

Use mathematical induction to prove the results of the following statements. In all cases $n \in \mathbb{Z}^+$ unless otherwise stated.

1   (i) $\sum_{r=1}^{n} r(r+1) = \frac{1}{3}n(n+1)(n+2)$.

   (ii) $\sum_{r=1}^{n} \frac{1}{r(r+1)} = \frac{n}{n+1}$.

   (iii) $\sum_{r=1}^{n} \frac{1}{(4r^2-1)} = \frac{n}{2n+1}$.

   (iv) $\sum_{r=1}^{n} r(r!) = (n+1)! - 1$.

   (v) $\sum_{r=1}^{n} r2^{r-1} = (n-1)2^n + 1$.

   (vi) $\sum_{r=1}^{n} (r^2+1)(r!) = n[(n+1)!]$.

   (vii) If $x > -1$, then $(1+x)^n \geqslant 1 + nx$.

2   (i) $\frac{d^n}{dx^n}[\sin(ax+b)] = a^n \sin(ax+b+n\pi/2)$.

   (ii) $\frac{d^n}{dx^n}[e^{cx}\sin(ax+b)] = (a^2+c^2)^{n/2}e^{cx}\sin(ax+b+n\theta)$,
     where $\sin\theta = a/\sqrt{(a^2+c^2)}$ and $\cos\theta = c/\sqrt{(a^2+c^2)}$.

*3 $\sum_{r=1}^{n} \cos r\theta = \frac{\sin\frac{1}{2}(2n+1)\theta}{2\sin\frac{1}{2}\theta} - \frac{1}{2}$, $\theta/2\pi \notin \mathbb{Z}$.

4   $\sum_{r=1}^{n} (r+1).r! = n.(n+1)!$

5   Given that the sequence (u_n) is defined by

$$u_{n+2} - 3u_{n+1} + 2u_n = 0,$$

where $u_1 = 3$, $u_2 = 7$, then $u_n = 2^{n+1} - 1$.

6   (i) $n^5 - n$ is divisible by 30, $(n > 1)$.
    (ii) $5^{2n} + 12^{n-1}$ is divisible by 13.
    (iii) $3 \cdot 7^{3n} + 2 \cdot 45^{n-1}$ is divisible by 8.
    (iv) $5^{2n+2} - 24n - 25$ is divisible by 576.

*7 $\left| \sum_{r=1}^{n} z_r \right| \leqslant \sum_{r=1}^{n} |z_r|.$

8   $\sum_{r=1}^{n} \dfrac{1}{r^2 - 1} = \dfrac{3}{4} - \dfrac{2n+1}{2n(n+1)}.$

9   The binomial theorem for a positive integral index, i.e.

$$(a + x)^n = a^n + na^{n-1} x + \binom{n}{2} a^{n-2} x^2 + \ldots + \binom{n}{r-1} a^{n-r+1} x^{r-1} + \ldots + x^n.$$

*10   If the function f satisfies the relations $f(x) \cdot f(y) = f(x + y)$ for all x, y and $f(0) = 1$, then show that

$$f(nx) = [f(x)]^n \quad \text{when}$$

(i) n is a positive integer,
(ii) n is a negative integer.
Give a particular function with this property.

4.7   Contradiction

In many cases it is possible to prove the result $p \Rightarrow q$ by assuming (p and $\sim q$) and obtaining a contradiction. It then follows that the assumption (p and $\sim q$) is impossible so that the hypothesis p must imply q or equivalently the hypothesis $\sim q$ must imply $\sim p$. We now give some examples illustrating this technique.

Example 24   To prove that $\sqrt{3}$ is not a rational number, i.e.

$$(x^2 = 3) \quad \Rightarrow \quad (x \text{ is an irrational number}).$$

This is based on the fact that for integers a, b:

$$(3 \text{ divides } ab) \quad \Rightarrow \quad (3 \text{ divides } a \text{ or } 3 \text{ divides } b).$$

Thus suppose $p : x^2 = 3$

and $\sim q : x = r/s, \quad r, s \in \mathbb{N},$

where $(r, s) = 1$, i.e. they have no factor in common other than 1.

Now $[(r/s)^2 = 3] \quad \Rightarrow \quad (r^2 = 3s^2)$

$\Rightarrow \quad (3 \text{ divides } r \times r)$

$\Rightarrow \quad (3 \text{ divides } r \text{ or } 3 \text{ divides } r)$

$\Rightarrow \quad (3 \text{ divides } r)$

and so $r = 3r'$ say. The equation now reduces to the form

$$3r'^2 = s^2.$$

This requires that 3 divides s by the same argument and so $(r, s) \geq 3$ since r and s have a factor 3 in common, contradicting $\sim q$. Thus p and $\sim q$ have led to a contradiction so that $p \Rightarrow q$.

But, sir, contradiction often **is** a proof.

Example 25 Given that $r \in \mathbb{R}$ and $r > 1$, show that, as $n \to \infty$, then $r^n \to \infty$.

Let $u_n = r^n$. Since $r > 1$, $u_{n+1} > u_n$, so that (u_n) is an increasing sequence. It is a property of increasing sequences that
either   (i) $u_n \to \infty$,
or   (ii) u_n converges, to l say, and $l \geq u_1$.
Since we are trying to prove (i), then (ii) should lead to a contradiction in which case (i) is the only remaining possibility. Let us assume (ii) that $r^n \to l$. Then

$$rl = r \lim_{n \to \infty} r^n = \lim_{n \to \infty} r^{n+1} = \lim_{n+1 \to \infty} r^{n+1} = l,$$

or $l(r - 1) = 0.$

Now $l \geq u_1 = r > 1$ and $r > 1$, so $l(r - 1) = 0$ gives a contradiction. Thus only (i) is possible and so $r^n \to \infty$ as $n \to \infty$.

Example 26 The number of primes is infinite.

Suppose the theorem is false and there exist just n primes, $p_1, p_2, \ldots, p_n$, say. Then consider N, where $N = 1 + p_1 p_2 \ldots p_n$.

Clearly N is not divisible by p_1, since it leaves a remainder 1 when divided by p_1. Similarly it is not divisible by $p_1, p_2, \ldots,$ or p_n.

Thus N has no prime factors, contrary to the property that any number can be expressed as the product of primes. Hence our contradiction and the assumption that the number of primes is finite must be false. It follows that the number of primes must be infinite.

Example 27 Prove that there is an infinite number of rational numbers between 0 and 1.

Suppose the theorem is false and that there exists a finite number of rationals between 0 and 1. Then there will be a greatest rational, say m/n, where $m < n$ and $m, n \in \mathbb{Z}^+$.

But $(m + 1)/(n + 1)$ is also rational and, since

$$1 - \frac{m+1}{n+1} = \frac{n-m}{n+1} > 0,$$

it lies between 0 and 1. Further

$$\frac{m+1}{n+1} - \frac{m}{n} = \frac{n-m}{n(n+1)} > 0$$

and so there is a rational number in $(0, 1)$ exceeding m/n. This contradicts the fact that m/n is the greatest rational between 0 and 1. Hence our assumption that the number of rationals between 0 and 1 is finite must be false. It follows that the number of rationals between 0 and 1 must be infinite.

Example 28
p: the opposite angles of a quadrilateral $ABCD$ are supplementary,
q: A, B, C, D lie on a circle.
Show that $p \Rightarrow q$.

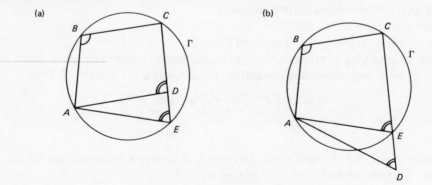

Fig. 4.8

Now, $q \Rightarrow p$ is a standard result which we assume.

Suppose p and $\sim q$, so that the circle Γ passing through A, B and C does not pass through D. Figures 4.8 (a) and (b) show the two possible cases. Let CD meet Γ in E (other than C). Join AE. Since $q \Rightarrow p$ and A, B, C, E are concyclic, then $\angle AEC$ is supplementary to $\angle ABC$. By p, $\angle ADC$ and $\angle ABC$ are supplementary and so $\angle AEC = \angle ADC$. The triangle AED has the exterior angle as the sum of the interior opposite angles and so $\angle EAD = 0$. Thus $D = E$, and this contradicts the fact that Γ does not pass through D.

p and $\sim q$ have led to a contradiction and so $p \Rightarrow q$.

Exercise 4.7
Prove, by the method of contradiction, the following results.
1　There is no greatest rational number less than $\sqrt{2}$.
*2　A polynomial of the nth degree has no more than n different roots.
3　In the triangle ABC, $AB^2 + BC^2 = AC^2$. Then $\angle ABC = 90°$.
**4　A rigid body is suspended freely from a fixed point A by a light inelastic string attached to A and to a fixed point on the surface of the body. Then, when the body hangs in equilibrium, the vertical through A passes through the centre of mass of the body.

4.8　Counter-example
If a proposition is suspected of being false, then one single counter-example is sufficient to prove this fact. Note that, although (in general) checking of particular cases will not prove a proposition, nevertheless just one counter-example is sufficient to prove that a proposition is false. For example, the fact that the first four odd integers, namely, 1, 3, 5 and 7, are prime does not prove that all odd numbers are prime! In fact, just one counter-example

Counter-example proof

$(9 = 3 \times 3)$ is sufficient to disprove this proposition. Here we give some more illustrative examples.

Example 29   It is known that, if the series $\sum\limits_{r=1}^{\infty} u_n$ converges, then $\lim\limits_{n\to\infty} u_n = 0$. Prove by a counter-example that the converse is false.

Consider $u_n = 1/\sqrt{n}$.
Clearly $u_n \to 0$ as $n \to \infty$.
But $u_1 > u_2 > u_3 > \ldots > u_n > \ldots$,
and so, for $n > 1$, $\sum\limits_{r=1}^{n} u_r > n \times 1/\sqrt{n} = \sqrt{n}$ which tends to ∞ as $n \to \infty$. Hence we have our counter-example.

Example 30   Prove that the following propositions are false by choosing counter-examples (**A**, **B** are 2×2 matrices).

(i) $(\mathbf{A} = \mathbf{A}^2) \Rightarrow (\mathbf{A} = \mathbf{O} \text{ or } \mathbf{I})$.
(ii) $(\mathbf{AB} = \mathbf{O}) \Rightarrow (\mathbf{A} = \mathbf{O} \text{ or } \mathbf{B} = \mathbf{O})$.
(iii) $\mathbf{A}^2 - \mathbf{B}^2 = (\mathbf{A} - \mathbf{B})(\mathbf{A} + \mathbf{B})$.

In (i) take $\mathbf{A} = \begin{pmatrix} 1 & 1 \\ 0 & 0 \end{pmatrix}$.

In (ii), (iii) take $\mathbf{A} = \begin{pmatrix} 1 & 1 \\ 1 & 1 \end{pmatrix}$, $\mathbf{B} = \begin{pmatrix} 1 & 0 \\ -1 & 0 \end{pmatrix}$.

Example 31   Disprove by a counter-example: if $f'(a) = 0$ then $f(x)$ has a maximum or minimum at a.

A function such as x^3 with graph such as the one shown in Fig. 4.9 is a sufficient counter-example.

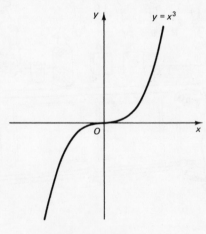

Fig. 4.9

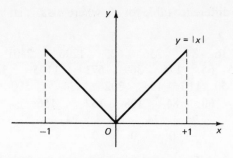

Fig. 4.10

Example 32 A function which is differentiable in (a, b) is continuous.

The converse is false as shown by the function $f(x) = |x|$ in the interval $(-1, 1)$ which is a sufficient counter-example as the derivative does not exist at $x = 0$. See Fig. 4.10.

Example 33 Suppose $f''(x)$ exists and the curve $y = f(x)$ has an inflexion where $x = a$. Then $f''(a) = 0$.

However the converse is false as shown by the counter-example with $f(x) = x^4$, where $f''(0) = 0$ but $f(x)$ has a minimum at $x = 0$.

Exercise 4.8
Show that the following statements are false.
1 $(a > b, c > d) \Rightarrow (ac > bd)$.
2 $(x < 1) \Rightarrow (x^2 < 1)$.
3 $(a < b + 1/n \; \forall n \in \mathbb{Z}^+) \Rightarrow (a < b)$.
*4 Matrix multiplication is commutative.
5 For a function f, $f'(a - h) < 0$ and $f'(a + h) > 0$ for $h \in \mathbb{R}^+$. Then f has a minimum at a.
6 $(\sin x > \sin y) \Rightarrow (x > y)$.
*7 $(\mathbf{AB} = \mathbf{C}) \Rightarrow (\mathbf{B} = \mathbf{A}^{-1}\mathbf{C})$ where $\mathbf{A}, \mathbf{B}, \mathbf{C}$ are 2×2 matrices.
**8 (A system of coplanar forces can be represented by the three sides of a triangle taken in order) $\Rightarrow$ (the system of forces is in equilibrium.)

4.9 Some miscellaneous methods

Analogy
Many examples exist of analogies between different branches of mathematics. For example, there is a close analogy between differentiation and finite differences extending to an analogy between the solution of differential equations and difference equations. We give a few examples illustrative of various analogies.

Example 34 The difference table for n^4, where $n \in \mathbb{Z}^+$, is:

n	1	2	3	4	5	6	7	8
n^4	1	16	81	256	625	1296	2401	4096
1st difference		15	65	175	369	671	1105	1695
2nd difference			50	110	194	302	434	590
3rd difference				60	84	108	132	156
4th difference					24	24	24	24
5th difference						0	0	0

Note that the fourth differences are constant and the fifth differences are zero (as they are for any fourth degree polynomial).

The analogy in differentiation is that $\dfrac{d^4}{dx^4}(x^4) = \text{constant}$ and $\dfrac{d^5}{dx^5}(x^4) = 0$.

Where we can spot an analogy we may find it useful to consider analogous methods of proof.

* *Example 35* Consider the solutions of the following second-order linear differential equations and second-order linear difference equations:

$$\frac{d^2y}{dx^2} + \frac{2dy}{dx} - 15y = 0 \qquad u_{n+2} + 2u_{n+1} - 15u_n = 0$$

Try $y = e^{mx}$. $\qquad\qquad$ Try $y = m^n$.

$y = C_1 e^{-5x} + C_2 e^{3x}$ $\qquad$ $u_n = C_1(-5)^n + C_2 3^n$.

In each case the auxiliary equation is $m^2 + 2m - 15 = 0$ with roots -5 and 3.

* *Example 36* Given that $f(x) > 0$ and $f'(x) < 0$ for $x \in \mathbb{R}^+$, then the series $\displaystyle\sum_{r=1}^{\infty} f(r)$ and the integral $\displaystyle\int_1^{\infty} f(x)\,dx$ both converge or both diverge.

** *Example 37* The parallel axis theorem for the radius of gyration, i.e. the moment of inertia of a body about any axis is equal to the moment of inertia about a parallel axis through the centre of mass together with the product of the mass of the body and the square of the distance between the axes. The radius of gyration is k where mass $\times k^2 = $ moment of inertia. This is equivalent to the equation

$$\sigma^2 = \frac{1}{n}\sum_{i=1}^{n}(x_i^2) - \left[\frac{1}{n}\sum_{i=1}^{n} x_i\right]^2$$

for the variance in statistics.

* *Example 38* If the polynomial equation $\displaystyle\sum_{r=0}^{n} a_r x^r = 0$ has coefficients in $\mathbb{Q}$ and has a root $a + b\sqrt{c}$, where $a, b, c \in \mathbb{Q}$ but $\sqrt{c} \notin \mathbb{Q}$, show that the polynomial equation also has a root $a - b\sqrt{c}$.

The question will perhaps call to mind the fact that if a polynomial equation $\sum_{r=0}^{n} a_r z^r = 0$ has coefficients in $\mathbb{R}$ and has a root $\alpha + \beta i$ where α, $\beta \in \mathbb{R}$, then it also has a root $\alpha - \beta i$, the conjugate $(\alpha + \beta i)^*$ of $\alpha + \beta i$.

The argument in this second case is based on the properties of complex conjugates

(i) $(z_1 + z_2)^* = z_1^* + z_2^*$,

(ii) $(z_1 z_2)^* = z_1^* z_2^*$,

(iii) $(z = 0) \Leftrightarrow (z^* = 0)$,

and the generalisations (iv) and (v) of (i) and (ii) to sums and products of r complex numbers which are proved by induction. The argument is

$$\left(\sum_{r=0}^{n} a_r z^r = 0 \right) \quad \Leftrightarrow \quad \left[\left(\sum_{r=0}^{n} a_r z^r \right)^* = 0 \right] \qquad \text{by (iii)}$$

$$\Leftrightarrow \quad \left[\sum_{r=0}^{n} (a_r z^r)^* = 0 \right] \qquad \text{by (iv)}$$

$$\Leftrightarrow \quad \left[\sum_{r=0}^{n} a_r^* (z^*)^r = 0 \right] \qquad \text{by (v)}$$

$$\Leftrightarrow \quad \left[\sum_{r=0}^{n} a_r (z^*)^r = 0 \right].$$

Let us see if we can adapt this argument for our question. Firstly we need a conjugate for $a + b\sqrt{c}$. Let us try

$$\text{conj}\,(a + b\sqrt{c}) = a - b\sqrt{c}.$$

First we must check (i), (ii) and (iii).

(i) $\text{conj}\,[(a_1 + b_1\sqrt{c}) + (a_2 + b_2\sqrt{c})] = \text{conj}\,[(a_1 + a_2) + (b_1 + b_2)\sqrt{c}]$

$$= a_1 + a_2 - (b_1 + b_2)\sqrt{c}$$

$$= (a_1 - b_1\sqrt{c}) + (a_2 - b_2\sqrt{c})$$

$$= \text{conj}\,(a_1 + b_1\sqrt{c})$$

$$\qquad + \text{conj}\,(a_2 + b_2\sqrt{c}).$$

(ii) $\quad \text{conj}\,[(a_1 + b_1\sqrt{c})(a_2 + b_2\sqrt{c})]$

$= \text{conj}\,[a_1 a_2 + b_1 b_2 c + (a_1 b_2 + a_2 b_1)\sqrt{c}]$

$= a_1 a_2 + b_1 b_2 c - (a_1 b_2 + a_2 b_1)\sqrt{c}$

$= (a_1 - b_1\sqrt{c})(a_2 - b_2\sqrt{c})$

$= \text{conj}\,(a_1 + b_1\sqrt{c}) . \text{conj}\,(a_2 + b_2\sqrt{c}).$

(iii) $(a + b\sqrt{c} = 0) \quad \Rightarrow \quad (b = 0 \text{ or } \sqrt{c} = -a/b).$

Now $(\sqrt{c} = -a/b) \Rightarrow (c = a^2/b^2) \Rightarrow (c \in \mathbb{Q})$, which is disallowed, and so $b = 0$ is the only possibility. Thus

$$(a + b\sqrt{c} = 0) \quad \Leftrightarrow \quad (b = 0 \text{ and } a = 0) \quad \Leftrightarrow \quad (a - b\sqrt{c} = 0),$$

or $\quad (a + b\sqrt{c} = 0) \quad \Leftrightarrow \quad (\text{conj}(a + b\sqrt{c}) = 0).$

The generalisation of (i) and (ii) to sums and products of r numbers of the form $a + b\sqrt{c}$ can again be proved by induction. The final argument becomes

$$\left[\sum_{r=0}^{n} \alpha_r (a + b\sqrt{c})^r = 0 \right] \quad \Leftrightarrow \quad \left[\text{conj} \left(\sum_{r=0}^{n} \alpha_r (a + b\sqrt{c})^r = 0 \right) \right]$$

$$\Leftrightarrow \quad \left[\sum_{r=0}^{n} \text{conj}(\alpha_r(a + b\sqrt{c})^r) = 0 \right]$$

$$\Leftrightarrow \quad \left[\sum_{r=0}^{n} \text{conj}(\alpha_r)(\text{conj}(a + b\sqrt{c}))^r = 0 \right]$$

$$\Leftrightarrow \quad \left[\sum_{r=0}^{n} \alpha_r (a - b\sqrt{c})^r = 0 \right].$$

Symmetry

Particularly in geometry, including curve sketching, and algebra, symmetry is extremely valuable since it reduces the work necessary and can act as a check.

Example 39 The groups

A, $\{1, i, -1, -i\}$ under multiplication,

B, $\left\{ \begin{pmatrix} 1 & 0 \\ 0 & 1 \end{pmatrix}, \begin{pmatrix} 0 & 1 \\ -1 & 0 \end{pmatrix}, \begin{pmatrix} -1 & 0 \\ 0 & -1 \end{pmatrix}, \begin{pmatrix} 0 & -1 \\ 1 & 0 \end{pmatrix} \right\}$ under matrix multiplication,

C, $\{1, 2, 4, 3\}$ under multiplication modulo 5,

D, $\{x, (1 + x)/(1 - x), -1/x, (x - 1)/(x + 1)\}$ of functions from $L = \mathbb{R} - \{0, 1, -1\}$ to L under functional composition,

E, $\{(1)(2)(3)(4), (1234), (13)(24), (1432)\}$ of permutations under composition, are all isomorphic and have group table

	e	a	b	c
e	e	a	b	c
a	a	b	c	e
b	b	c	e	a
c	c	e	a	b

The symmetry of this table about the leading diagonal indicates that the groups are abelian.

Example 40 The curve C, with equation $y^2 = x^2(4 - x^2)$, is symmetric about each of the coordinate axes. Changing x into $-x$ and/or y into $-y$ does not alter the equation of the curve. Thus $[(x, y) \in C] \Leftrightarrow [(-x, y) \in C]$, etc.

Example 41 Given that α, β, γ are the roots of the equation

$$x^3 + px + q = 0, \quad q \neq 0, \qquad (4.6)$$

and $s_n = \alpha^n + \beta^n + \gamma^n$, where $n \in \mathbb{Z}$, show that

$$s_{n+3} + ps_{n+1} + qs_n = 0.$$

Since $q \neq 0$, zero is not a root of (4.6) and so what follows also holds for $n \in \mathbb{Z}^-$.
Putting $x = \alpha$ in (4.6) we have $\alpha^3 + p\alpha + q = 0$.
Multiplication by α^n gives $\alpha^{n+3} + p\alpha^{n+1} + q\alpha^n = 0$.
Similarly (and this is the important symmetry word!)

$$\beta^{n+3} + p\beta^{n+1} + q\beta^n = 0,$$

$$\gamma^{n+3} + p\gamma^{n+1} + q\gamma^n = 0.$$

Addition gives the required result.

Example 42 Express as a product of factors the determinant Δ, where

$$\Delta = \begin{vmatrix} 1 & a & a^2 \\ 1 & b & b^2 \\ 1 & c & c^2 \end{vmatrix}.$$

Δ is a homogeneous polynomial of degree 3 in a, b and c and

$$(a = b \text{ gives two rows identical, so } \Delta = 0) \Rightarrow [(a - b) \text{ is a factor of } \Delta].$$

By symmetry, $(b - c)$ and $(c - a)$ are also factors of Δ. It follows that

$$\Delta = k(a - b)(b - c)(c - a),$$

where k does not depend upon a, b or c. Comparing the coefficient of bc^2
gives $k = 1$.

Exercise 4.9

1 Plot the curves $y = \sin x \,(-\pi/2 \leqslant x \leqslant \pi/2)$ and $y = \sin^{-1} x \,(-1 \leqslant x \leqslant 1)$ on the same
diagram.

2 If f is an odd function, show that

$$\int_{-a}^{a} f(x)\,dx = 0.$$

If f is an even function show that

$$\int_{-a}^{a} f(x)\,dx = 2 \int_{0}^{a} f(x)\,dx.$$

3 Use the fact that $\sin(\pi - x) = \sin x$ and the substitution $\pi - x = u$ to evaluate

$$\int_{0}^{\pi} x \sin x\,dx.$$

**4 Find the expected value of the random variable whose continuous probability density function is given by

$$f(x) = 6x(1 - x), \quad 0 < x < 1,$$
$$= 0 \qquad \text{elsewhere.}$$

5 Prove that $a^2(b - c) + b^2(c - a) + c^2(a - b) = -(b - c)(c - a)(a - b)$.

6 Prove that $a^3(b - c) + b^3(c - a) + c^3(a - b) = -(b - c)(c - a)(a - b)(a + b + c)$.

*7 Prove that $\begin{vmatrix} 1 & 1 & 1 \\ 1 & r & r^2 \\ 1 & r^2 & r^4 \end{vmatrix} = r(r - 1)^2(r^2 - 1)$.

8 Prove that the joins of the mid-points of the opposite edges of a tetrahedron intersect and bisect each other. (*Hint:* In tetrahedron $ABCD$ take O as the origin and the position vectors of A, B, C and D referred to O as $\mathbf{a}$, $\mathbf{b}$, $\mathbf{c}$ and $\mathbf{d}$ respectively. Then show that the mid-points $(\mathbf{a} + \mathbf{b})/2$ and $(\mathbf{c} + \mathbf{d})/2$ of opposite edges have mid-point with position vector $\frac{1}{4}(\mathbf{a} + \mathbf{b} + \mathbf{c} + \mathbf{d})$.)

9 Prove that the lines joining the vertices of a tetrahedron to the centroids of the opposite faces intersect and divide each other in the ratio $3 : 1$.

10 A, B, C are points on the parabola $y^2 = 4ax$, with ordinates y_1, y_2, y_3, respectively. Show that the area of $\triangle ABC$ is $|(y_1 - y_2)(y_2 - y_3)(y_3 - y_1)/(8a)|$. [*Hint:* use a similar method to that of example 42 above.]

4.10   A formal strategy for proof

All our proof questions are of the form, or can be written in the form

'Show that $P \Rightarrow Q$'.

P can be thought of as a statement indicating the conditions of the problem, and they will usually be in the form of several requirements $(P_1, P_2, \ldots, P_n)$. In trying to prove Q we can call upon various basic properties A (axioms) which are assumed to hold, where $A = (A_1, A_2, \ldots, A_m)$, and also various standard results T (theorems), where $T = (T_1, T_2, \ldots, T_k)$, which have been established at some earlier stage in the development of the theory. We group together all the hypotheses and theorems as

$$(P, A, T) = (P_1, P_2, \ldots, P_n, A_1, \ldots, A_m, T_1, \ldots, T_k)$$

although at any stage we may only be using a subset of these. The first line of our proof will be of the form

$$(P, A, T) \Rightarrow (Q_1),$$

and subsequent lines

$$(P, A, T, Q_1, Q_2, \ldots, Q_{i-1}) \Rightarrow Q_i, \quad i = 2, 3, \ldots, p,$$

with $Q_p = Q$. Each line of the argument involves some of the requirements P, axioms A, theorems T, and previously established results $Q_1, Q_2, \ldots, Q_{i-1}$.

Let us consider a simple example.

Show that $(n \in \mathbb{Z}^+) \Rightarrow (2^n > n)$.

Here we have $\quad p: n \in \mathbb{Z}^+$,
$$q: 2^n > n.$$
The conditions P of the problem in this case are just one, namely p. The axioms A are the axioms of the real numbers, which we apply as second nature, i.e. statements such as $(a > b, b > c) \Rightarrow (a > c)$.

The theorems here are

T_1 : the binomial theorem

$$(1 + x)^n = \sum_{r=0}^{n} \binom{n}{r} x^r \qquad \text{for } n \in \mathbb{Z}^+,$$

and $\qquad T_2 : \binom{n}{r} = \dfrac{n!}{(n-r)!\,r!} > 0 \quad \text{for } 0 \leqslant r \leqslant n, n \in \mathbb{Z}^+.$

Putting $x = 1$, the first step of the proof is

$$(P, A, T_1) \Rightarrow Q_1,$$

where

$$Q_1 : (1 + 1)^n = \sum_{r=0}^{n} \binom{n}{r}.$$

The second step is to use T_2. Thus

$$(P, A, T_2, Q_1) \Rightarrow Q_2,$$

where

$$Q_2 : 2^n > \binom{n}{1},$$

since the sum of $n + 1$ positive terms is greater than the one corresponding to $r = 1$. Q_2 is q so we have our proof.

In reality we do not write out the proof in such detail. In fact, exhibiting the proof in too much detail can make it much harder to read. Sufficient understanding would allow:

By the binomial theorem we have, for $n \in \mathbb{Z}^+$,

$$2^n = (1 + 1)^n = \sum_{r=0}^{n} \binom{n}{r} 1^r > \binom{n}{1} = n.$$

We can prove $P \Rightarrow Q$ by considering $\sim Q \Rightarrow \sim P$ or by considering (P and $\sim Q$) and arguing to a contradiction, but in all cases the steps in our argument are as indicated above.

5 Writing out a proof

In this chapter we give a number of examples illustrating how a proof should be written out (particularly in the context of examinations). Each example is followed by notes and comment but this is for your benefit and to enable you to understand what has been done. In chapter 6 some of the same examples will be reconsidered and some common errors pointed out.

Example 1   Given that $\mathbf{A}$, $\mathbf{B}$ are $n \times n$ matrices, and $\mathbf{AB} = \mathbf{A}$, $\mathbf{BA} = \mathbf{B}$ show that $\mathbf{A}$ and $\mathbf{B}$ are idempotent. (An idempotent matrix $\mathbf{X}$ is such that $\mathbf{X}^2 = \mathbf{X}$.)

$$\mathbf{A}^2 = (\mathbf{AB})(\mathbf{AB}) = [(\mathbf{AB})\mathbf{A}]\mathbf{B}$$
$$= [\mathbf{A}(\mathbf{BA})]\mathbf{B} = [\mathbf{AB}]\mathbf{B}$$
$$= \mathbf{AB} = \mathbf{A}.$$

By symmetry (or replacing $\mathbf{A}$, $\mathbf{B}$ by $\mathbf{B}$, $\mathbf{A}$ respectively in the above argument)

$$\mathbf{B}^2 = \mathbf{B}.$$

Notes: The method of proof is clear (the use of brackets indicating how the proof has developed). The symmetry lies in the fact that the hypotheses are unchanged by an interchange of $\mathbf{A}$ and $\mathbf{B}$ and so the conclusion $\mathbf{A}^2 = \mathbf{A}$ implies a second conclusion $\mathbf{B}^2 = \mathbf{B}$.

Example 2   Using the definitions of $\sinh x$ and $\cosh x$ in terms of exponential functions, prove that

$$\cosh x \cosh y + \sinh x \sinh y \equiv \cosh(x + y).$$

$\cosh x \cosh y + \sinh x \sinh y$

$$\equiv \tfrac{1}{2}(e^x + e^{-x}) \cdot \tfrac{1}{2}(e^y + e^{-y}) + \tfrac{1}{2}(e^x - e^{-x}) \cdot \tfrac{1}{2}(e^y - e^{-y})$$
$$\equiv \tfrac{1}{4}(e^{x+y} + e^{-x+y} + e^{x-y} + e^{-x-y} + e^{x+y} - e^{-x+y} - e^{x-y} + e^{-x-y})$$
$$\equiv \tfrac{1}{2}(e^{x+y} + e^{-x-y})$$
$$\equiv \cosh(x + y).$$

Note: All hyperbolic identities may be proved in this way.

Example 3   Prove that, for all values of θ, $\phi \in \mathbb{R}$,

$$\sin^2\theta\cos^2\phi - \cos^2\theta\sin^2\phi = \sin^2\theta - \sin^2\phi. \tag{5.1}$$

$$\sin^2\theta\cos^2\phi - \cos^2\theta\sin^2\phi = \sin^2\theta(1 - \sin^2\phi) - (1 - \sin^2\theta)\sin^2\phi$$

$$= \sin^2\theta - \sin^2\theta\sin^2\phi - \sin^2\phi + \sin^2\theta\sin^2\phi$$

$$= \sin^2\theta - \sin^2\phi.$$

Note that, although (5.1) is true for θ, $\phi \in \mathbb{R}$, we cannot write

$$\frac{\sin^2\theta\cos^2\phi - \cos^2\theta\sin^2\phi}{\sin^2\theta - \sin^2\phi} \equiv 1$$

without qualification. We must specify, on dividing equality (5.1) by $(\sin^2\theta - \sin^2\phi)$, that $(\sin^2\theta - \sin^2\phi) \neq 0$.

Example 4 Given that $y = [x + \sqrt{(1 + x^2)}]^{1/2}$, show that

$$(1 + x^2)\frac{d^2y}{dx^2} + x\frac{dy}{dx} - \frac{1}{4}y = 0.$$

$$[y^2 = x + \sqrt{(1 + x^2)}] \quad \Rightarrow \quad \left[2y\frac{dy}{dx} = 1 + x(1 + x^2)^{-1/2} = \frac{y^2}{\sqrt{(1 + x^2)}}\right]$$

$$\Rightarrow \quad \left[\frac{dy}{dx} = \frac{y}{2\sqrt{(1 + x^2)}}\right]$$

$$\Rightarrow \quad \left[\left(\frac{dy}{dx}\right)^2 = \frac{y^2}{4(1 + x^2)}\right]$$

$$\Rightarrow \quad \left[(1 + x^2)\left(\frac{dy}{dx}\right)^2 = \frac{1}{4}y^2\right]$$

$$\Rightarrow \quad \left[(1 + x^2)2\frac{dy}{dx}\cdot\frac{d^2y}{dx^2} + 2x\left(\frac{dy}{dx}\right)^2 = \frac{1}{4}\cdot 2y\frac{dy}{dx}\right],$$

where the last implication involves differentiating the previous equation. Cancellation of $2\frac{dy}{dx}(\neq 0)$ gives the required result.

Note: (i) We have not obtained the result by simply differentiating the original function twice and substituting in the differential equation. This method is available but tends to involve rather more complicated differentiations.

(ii) When $y = \sqrt{}$(compound expression), it is nearly always easier to differentiate y^2, but care must be taken in cases where the sign matters as one is also finding $\frac{dy}{dx}$ for $y = -\sqrt{}$.

Example 5 Given that $a, b, c, d \in \mathbb{R}$ prove that
 (i) $a^2 + b^2 \geqslant 2ab$,
 (ii) $a^4 + b^4 + c^4 + d^4 \geqslant 4abcd$.

(i) $\qquad [(a - b)^2 \geqslant 0] \quad \Rightarrow \quad [a^2 + b^2 - 2ab \geqslant 0]$

$$\Rightarrow \quad [a^2 + b^2 \geqslant 2ab].$$

Note: If we write $x = a^2$ and $y = b^2$ we obtain the inequality $\frac{1}{2}(x + y) \geqslant \sqrt{(xy)}$, relating the arithmetic and geometric means of two positive numbers x and y.

(ii) Using (i) with a^2 and b^2 in place of a and b respectively etc.,

$$a^4 + b^4 \geqslant 2a^2b^2, \quad c^4 + d^4 \geqslant 2c^2d^2.$$

This gives

$$a^4 + b^4 + c^4 + d^4 \geqslant 2(a^2b^2 + c^2d^2). \tag{5.2}$$

By (i)

$$a^2b^2 + c^2d^2 \geqslant 2(ab)(cd) = 2abcd. \tag{5.3}$$

By (5.2) and (5.3)

$$a^4 + b^4 + c^4 + d^4 \geqslant 4abcd.$$

Note: Here we see how we use the basic result (i) to prove more elaborate results. (In examinations you are often asked to prove a basic result followed by a more difficult one. You should always look and see whether the simple result can be used for the second part, as the examiner is frequently guiding you to the best possible method to use.)

Example 6 Find the solution set of the inequalities

$$0 < \frac{x(2 + x)}{2x + 1} < 1.$$

Multiplying through by $(2x + 1)^2$ gives

$$0 < x(2 + x)(2x + 1) < (2x + 1)^2.$$

The first (left-hand) inequality requires

$$x > 0 \text{ or } -2 < x < -\tfrac{1}{2}. \tag{5.4}$$

The second (right-hand) inequality requires

$[x(2 + x)(2x + 1) < (2x + 1)^2] \quad \Leftrightarrow \quad [(2x + 1)(x(2 + x) - (2x + 1)) < 0]$

$$\Leftrightarrow \quad [(2x + 1)(x + 1)(x - 1) < 0]$$

$$\Leftrightarrow \quad [x < -1 \text{ or } -\tfrac{1}{2} < x < 1]. \tag{5.5}$$

The intervals common to (5.4) and (5.5) are

$$-2 < x < -1 \quad \text{and} \quad 0 < x < 1$$

The solution set is $\{x: -2 < x < -1\} \cup \{x: 0 < x < 1\}$.

Notes: (i) We consider the two parts of the inequality separately and transform the right-hand inequality into an inequality with zero on one side. This is easier to deal with than the original since we then have only to consider the sign of the factors of the various terms.

(ii) A rough sketch graph of $y = x(2 + x)/(2x + 1)$ serves as a useful confirmation of our result. (See Fig. 5.1)

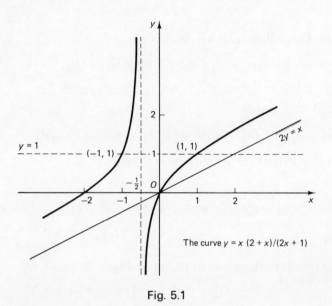

The curve $y = x (2 + x)/(2x + 1)$

Fig. 5.1

(iii) Since we asked for the solution set, we give our answer in set form.

Example 7 Solve for $\theta \in \mathbb{R}$, the equation

$$\sin \theta° + 2 \cos \theta° = 1.$$

The equation can be written

$$\sqrt{5} \sin (\theta° + \alpha°) = 1,$$

where $\cos \alpha° = 1/\sqrt{5}$, $\sin \alpha° = 2/\sqrt{5} \Rightarrow \alpha \approx 63.43$.

$(\sin \theta° + 2 \cos \theta° = 1) \quad \Leftrightarrow \quad [\sin (\theta° + \alpha°) = 1/\sqrt{5} \approx 0.4472]$

$\Leftrightarrow \quad [\theta + \alpha = 180n + (-1)^n 26.57 \text{ for some } n \in \mathbb{Z}]$

$\Leftrightarrow \quad (\theta = 360n + 90 \text{ or } 360n - 36.86 \text{ for some } n \in \mathbb{Z}).$

Alternatively we express the equation in terms of t, where $t = \tan (\theta/2)$, so that

$$\left(\frac{2t}{1 + t^2} + \frac{2(1 - t^2)}{1 + t^2} = 1 \right)$$

$$\Leftrightarrow \quad (3t^2 - 2t - 1 = 0)$$

$$\Leftrightarrow \quad [(3t + 1)(t - 1) = 0]$$

$$\Leftrightarrow \quad (t = -\tfrac{1}{3} \text{ or } t = 1)$$

$$\Leftrightarrow \quad [\theta/2 = 180n - 18\cdot43 \text{ or } 180n + 45 \text{ for some } n \in \mathbb{Z}]$$

$$\Leftrightarrow \quad [\theta = 360n - 36\cdot86 \text{ or } 360n + 90 \text{ for some } n \in \mathbb{Z}].$$

Example 8 Given that $z_1, z_2 \in \mathbb{C}$, prove that
$$\left| |z_1| - |z_2| \right| \leqslant |z_1 + z_2| \leqslant |z_1| + |z_2|.$$
Let $z_1 = x_1 + iy_1$, $z_2 = x_2 + iy_2$, where $x_1, y_1, x_2, y_2 \in \mathbb{R}$.

$$(|z_1| + |z_2|)^2 - |z_1 + z_2|^2$$
$$= [\sqrt{(x_1^2 + y_1^2)} + \sqrt{(x_2^2 + y_2^2)}]^2 - [(x_1 + x_2)^2 + (y_1 + y_2)^2]$$
$$= 2[\sqrt{(x_1^2 + y_1^2)}\sqrt{(x_2^2 + y_2^2)} - (x_1 x_2 + y_1 y_2)]$$

But

$$(x_1^2 + y_1^2)(x_2^2 + y_2^2) - (x_1 x_2 + y_1 y_2)^2 = x_1^2 y_2^2 - 2x_1 x_2 y_1 y_2 + x_2^2 y_1^2$$
$$= (x_1 y_2 - x_2 y_1)^2 \geqslant 0.$$

Taking the positive square root of the inequality

$$(x_1^2 + y_1^2)(x_2^2 + y_2^2) \geqslant (x_1 x_2 + y_1 y_2)^2,$$

gives
$$\sqrt{(x_1{}^2 + y_1{}^2)}\sqrt{(x_2{}^2 + y_2{}^2)} \geqslant |(x_1 x_2 + y_1 y_2)|,$$

and so
$$(|z_1| + |z_2|)^2 \geqslant |z_1 + z_2|^2.$$

Taking the positive square root gives

$$|z_1| + |z_2| \geqslant |z_1 + z_2| \tag{5.6}$$

as required.

Writing $z_1 + z_2$ in place of z_1 and $-z_2$ in place of z_2 we find

$$(|z_1 + z_2| + |-z_2| \geqslant |z_1 + z_2 - z_2|)$$

$$\Leftrightarrow \quad (|z_1 + z_2| \geqslant |z_1| - |z_2|) \quad (\text{since } |-z_2| = |z_2|). \tag{5.7}$$

Interchanging z_1 and z_2 in (5.7), i.e. using symmetry, we find

$$|z_1 + z_2| \geqslant |z_2| - |z_1|. \tag{5.8}$$

Inequalities (5.7) and (5.8) both hold iff

$$|z_1 + z_2| \geqslant \left| |z_1| - |z_2| \right|.$$

Notes: (i) By writing $z_1 - z_2$ in place of z_1 in equation (5.6), we find

$$|z_1 - z_2| \geqslant |z_1| - |z_2|$$

which is, of course, equation (5.7) with $-z_2$ written in place of z_2.

(ii) All the modulus inequalities can be illustrated geometrically and follow from the Euclidean theorem that the length of one side of a triangle cannot exceed the sum of the lengths of the other two sides.

(iii) These inequalities hold for the special case when $y_1 = 0 = y_2$, i.e. when z_1, z_2 are real.

*(iv) This theorem is of value in locating roots of equations. For example, consider the equation $z^4 + z + 2 = 0$.

Since

$$|z^4 + z + 2| \geqslant |2| - |z^4 + z|,$$

and

$$|z^4 + z| \leqslant |z^4| + |z| = |z|^4 + |z|,$$

it follows that

$$|z^4 + z + 2| \geqslant 2 - |z|^4 - |z|.$$

Therefore, for $|z| < 1$, $|z^4 + z + 2| > 0$.

It follows that the equation $z^4 + z + 2 = 0$ cannot have a root within the circle $|z| = 1$. (Remember that a complex number is zero iff its modulus is zero.) Prove similarly that $|z^4 + z + 2| \geqslant |z|^4 - |z| - 2$ and hence that all four roots of the equation lie inside the circle $|z| = 3/2$ (for example).

Example 9 Given that $I_n = \displaystyle\int_0^x t^n \cos t \, dt$, for $n \in \mathbb{N}$, prove the reduction formula

$$I_n = x^n \sin x + nx^{n-1} \cos x - n(n-1)I_{n-2} \quad \text{for } n \geqslant 2.$$

$$\left(I_n = \int_0^x t^n \frac{d}{dt}(\sin t) \, dt \right.$$

$$= \left[t^n \sin t \right]_0^x - \int_0^x \frac{d}{dt}(t^n) \sin t \, dt$$

$$= x^n \sin x - n \int_0^x t^{n-1} \sin t \, dt$$

$$= x^n \sin x - n \int_0^x t^{n-1} \frac{d}{dt}(-\cos t) \, dt$$

$$= x^n \sin x + \left[nt^{n-1} \cos t \right]_0^x - n \int_0^x \frac{d}{dt}(t^{n-1}) \cos t \, dt$$

$$\left. = x^n \sin x + nx^{n-1} \cos x - n(n-1) \int_0^x t^{n-2} \cos t \, dt \right)$$

$$\Rightarrow \quad (I_n = x^n \sin x + nx^{n-1} \cos x - n(n-1)I_{n-2}).$$

Notes: (i) Here we have needed to integrate by parts twice. The form of the answer suggests that this is the way forward.

(ii) A useful method when the reduction formula is for an indefinite integral is to start from the given result and proceed as follows:

$$\frac{d}{dt}(t^n \sin t + nt^{n-1} \cos t)$$

$$= t^n \cos t + nt^{n-1} \sin t - nt^{n-1} \sin t + n(n-1)t^{n-2} \cos t$$

$$= t^n \cos t + n(n-1)t^{n-2} \cos t.$$

Integrating from 0 to x gives

$$\left[t^n \sin t + nt^{n-1} \cos t \right]_0^x = I_n + n(n-1)I_{n-2},$$

which, on rearrangement is the required result.

Two similar examples for the reader to try are:

(a) $I_n = \displaystyle\int_0^x t^n (t^2 + c^2)^{-1/2} \, dt$,

$$nI_n + (n-1)c^2 I_{n-2} = x^{n-1}(x^2 + c^2)^{1/2},$$

(b) $I_n = \displaystyle\int_0^x e^{-t} \sin^n t \, dt$,

$$(n^2 + 1)I_n = -e^{-x}(\sin^n x + n\sin^{n-1} x \cos x) + n(n-1)I_{n-2}.$$

Example 10 Show that the line $lx + my + n = 0$ touches the parabola $y^2 = 4ax$ iff $am^2 = nl$.

Method 1 The intersection of the line and the curve is found by solving the simultaneous equations:

$$lx + my + n = 0,$$

$$y^2 = 4ax.$$

Eliminating x gives $\qquad\qquad ly^2 = 4alx = 4a(-my - n)$

or $\qquad\qquad\qquad\qquad ly^2 + 4amy + 4an = 0.$

The line touches the parabola if and only if this equation has equal roots.

$$(\text{This equation has equal roots}) \quad \Leftrightarrow \quad (4a^2 m^2 = 4aln)$$

$$\Leftrightarrow \quad (am^2 = ln).$$

Method 2 The tangent to the parabola $y^2 = 4ax$ at the point (x_1, y_1) is

$$2ax - y_1 y + 2ax_1 = 0. \tag{5.9}$$

Suppose this is the line

$$lx + my + n = 0. \tag{5.10}$$

[(5.9) and (5.10) are the same line] $\Leftrightarrow$ $(2a/l = -y_1/m = 2ax_1/n)$

$\Leftrightarrow$ $(x_1 = n/l, y_1 = -2ma/l)$. (5.11)

The equations (5.9) and (5.10) must be identical except perhaps for a multiplying factor and so the coefficients in the two equations must be proportional.
But (x_1, y_1) lies on the parabola, so that

$$y_1{}^2 = 4ax_1. \tag{5.12}$$

Substitution from (5.11) in (5.12) gives

$$4a^2m^2/l^2 = 4an/l$$

or
$$am^2 = nl. \tag{5.13}$$

In this method we have proved that $lx + my + n = 0$ is a tangent to the parabola only if $am^2 = nl$ (i.e. that the condition is necessary). However, the above argument is reversible thus,

Equation (5.13) implies that the point (x_1, y_1) defined by equation (5.11) lies on the parabola. Further, the tangent to the parabola at (x_1, y_1) is identical with equation (5.10) which proves that the condition is sufficient, i.e. the line (5.10) is a tangent if $am^2 = nl$.

Note: This example illustrates the reversible nature of most proofs by coordinate geometry as suggested on page 29.

Example 11   Prove that f(x), where

$$f(x) = \sin mx - \sin nx, \quad m^2 \neq n^2,$$

is periodic iff m/n is rational. Note that f is periodic iff there exists a positive number t such that

$$f(x + t) - f(x - t) \equiv 0. \tag{5.14}$$

Now

(5.14) $\Leftrightarrow$ $[(\sin m(x + t) - \sin m(x - t)) - (\sin n(x + t) - \sin n(x - t)) \equiv 0]$

$\Leftrightarrow$ $(\cos mx \sin mt - \cos nx \sin nt \equiv 0)$

$\Leftrightarrow$ $(\sin mt = 0 = \sin nt)$

$\Leftrightarrow$ $(mt = p\pi, nt = q\pi$ for some $p, q \in \mathbb{Z})$

$\Leftrightarrow$ $(m/n = p/q$ for some $p, q \in \mathbb{Z})$

$\Leftrightarrow$ $(m/n \in \mathbb{Q})$.

The third implication above follows by considering two suitable values of x, say $x = 0$ and $x = \pi/[2 \max(|m|, |n|)]$.

Exercise 5

1 Given that $\mathbf{M} = \begin{pmatrix} 1 & a \\ 0 & 1 \end{pmatrix}$, prove by induction that, when $n \in \mathbb{Z}^+$,

$$\mathbf{M}^n = \begin{pmatrix} 1 & na \\ 0 & 1 \end{pmatrix}.$$

*2 Given that m and $n \in \mathbb{Z}^+$ prove that

$$x^m(b^n - c^n) + b^m(c^n - x^n) + c^m(x^n - b^n)$$

is divisible by $x^2 - x(b + c) + bc$.

3 Prove that, for $n \in \mathbb{Z}^+$, the number $(7^n + 3^n + 6)$ is a multiple of 8.

4 Prove by induction that, for $n \in \mathbb{Z}^+$, the integer

$$5^{2n} + 3n - 1$$

is divisible by 9.

5 Show by induction, or otherwise, that

$$\sum_{r=1}^{n} \cos 2r\theta = \frac{\sin(2n+1)\theta}{2 \sin \theta} - \frac{1}{2} \qquad \frac{\theta}{\pi} \notin \mathbb{Z}$$

*6 Prove that $\sqrt{2} \notin \mathbb{Q}$. Show that a necessary and sufficient condition for $\sqrt{2} - 1$ to be a root of the cubic equation $az^3 - bz + c = 0$, where a, b and $c \in \mathbb{Q}$, is that $a : b : c = 1 : 5 : 2$.

7 Show that $(x - y)$ is a factor of $x^n - y^n$, where $n \in \mathbb{Z}^+$. Hence, prove that
   (i) $3 \times 9^n + 4 \times 2^n$ is a multiple of 7,
   (ii) $9^{n+3} + 4^n$ is a multiple of 5.

8 Given that $n \in \mathbb{Z}^+$, use the identity

$$F(n) \equiv n^4 + 2n^3 + 2n^2 + n \equiv n(n+1)(n+2)^2 - 3n(n+1)^2$$

to show that $F(n)$ is a multiple of 6. Use the binomial theorem to show that

$$(n+1)^5 = n^5 + 1 + 5F(n).$$

Hence prove by induction that, if $n > 1$, $n^5 - n$ is a multiple of 30.

*9 The rth term of a sequence is $4/(4r^2 - 1)$. Prove that the sum S_n of the first n terms of the sequence is given by

$$S_n = 4n/(2n + 1).$$

Show that

$$0 < \frac{4}{4r^2 - 1} - \frac{1}{r^2} \le \frac{1}{4r^2 - 1}, \quad \text{for } r \in \mathbb{N}.$$

Deduce that the error in the approximate formula

$$S_n \approx 1^{-2} + 2^{-2} + \ldots + n^{-2}$$

cannot exceed $S_n/4$.

*10 Prove that $3^{4n} + 2^{4n+1} \equiv 3 \pmod 5$.

11 Find the coordinates of the point on the curve $y = e^x$ at which the gradient is k, where $k > 0$.

Deduce that the equation of the tangent to the curve at this point is $y = kx + k \ln(e/k)$ and find the equation of the tangent which passes through the origin.

64 *Proof*

Find the range of values of c for which the equation $e^x = cx$ has two real solutions.

*12   Given that $a_1, a_2, \ldots, a_{n-1}$ are all positive, find the minimum value of $f(x)$, where

$$f(x) = \frac{(a_1 + a_2 + \ldots + a_{n-1} + x)/n}{(a_1 a_2 \ldots a_{n-1} x)^{1/n}} \quad \text{for all } x > 0.$$

Show also that this is the least value of $f(x)$ for all $x > 0$.

Use this result to prove, by induction, that

$$(a_1 a_2 \ldots a_n)^{1/n} \leqslant (a_1 + a_2 + \ldots + a_n)/n$$

for all positive $a_1, a_2, \ldots, a_n$ and all positive integers n.

*13   Let S be the set $\{a + b\sqrt{7}, a, b \in \mathbb{Q}\}$. Investigate each of the following assertions concerning the roots α, β of the equation $x^2 + 2px + q = 0$ (where p and q are non-zero and $p, q \in \mathbb{Q}$) either proving the assertion or disproving it by means of a counterexample.

(i) If $p^2 - q = 7$ then $\alpha, \beta \in S$,

(ii) If $\alpha, \beta \in S$ then $p^2 - q = 7$.

*14   Prove that the cube of every integer can be expressed as $9n$ or $9n \pm 1$, where $n \in \mathbb{Z}$.

Deduce that 9 is a factor of $\sum_{r=1}^{50} r^3$.

Given that $x, y,$ and $z \in \mathbb{Z}$, show that $x^3 + y^3 + z^3$ cannot be of the form $9n \pm 4$.

Given also that $x + y + z$ is a multiple of 3, show that $x^3 + y^3 + z^3$ cannot be of the form $9n \pm 1$, nor of the form $9n \pm 2$.

*15   Given that $m^n = 1$ and $m \neq 1$, prove that

$$1 + m + m^2 + \ldots + m^{n-1} = 0.$$

The function f is defined by $f(x) = mx + c$ where m and c are non-zero constants; $f_2(x)$ is defined as $f[f(x)]$ and other iterates similarly. By considering f_2, f_3, etc., suggest a form for $f_k(x)$ and decide by induction whether your suggested form is correct.

Show that the set $\{f_n : n \in \mathbb{Z}^+\}$ with the operation $*$, where $f_r * f_s = f_{r+s}$, forms a finite group if and only if m is a root of unity other than 1.

*16   Given that the lengths of n straight lines are 1 cm, 2 cm, $\ldots, n$ cm, there being one line of each length, show, by induction or otherwise, that the number, N_n, of proper triangles which can be formed by choosing three of them is

$$(n-2)n(2n-5)/24 \text{ if } n = 2p,$$

$$(n-3)(n-1)(2n-1)/24 \text{ if } n = 2p-1, \quad \text{where } p \in \mathbb{Z}^+.$$

17   Show that $[r(r+1)]^2 - [(r-1)r]^2 \equiv 4r^3$. Hence, or otherwise, find the sum of the cubes of the first n positive integers.

Find the sum of the first n terms of the series

$$1^3 + 3^3 + 5^3 + \ldots + (2r-1)^3 + \ldots.$$

18   Given that

$$y = e^{x \cos \alpha} \sin(x \sin \alpha)$$

prove by induction that

$$\frac{d^n y}{dx^n} = e^{x \cos \alpha} \sin(x \sin \alpha + n\alpha).$$

Hence obtain the Maclaurin series for y in ascending powers of x. Use this series to evaluate y, to 5 decimal places, when $x = 0.01$ and $\alpha = \pi/4$.

*19 n points are fixed in space and a straight line l passes through p of them where $1 \leqslant p \leqslant n$. No straight line other than l passes through more than two of the points. Show that the number of straight lines, including l, which pass through at least two of the points is

$$\tfrac{1}{2}(n - p)(n + p - 1) + 1.$$

*20 A sports programme of n items is to be formed in such a way that races P and Q are separated by exactly r races, where $r \leqslant n - 2$. Prove that the number of ways of arranging the programme is $2(n - 2)!(n - r - 1)$.

21 The normal at the point $(at^2, 2at)$ to the parabola $y^2 = 4ax$ meets the parabola again at the point $(ap^2, 2ap)$. Prove that

$$t^2 + tp + 2 = 0$$

and hence that $p^2 \geqslant 8$.

*22 Given that

$$(1 + x)^n = \sum_{r=0}^{n} c_r x^r,$$

where $n \in \mathbb{Z}^+$, prove that

$$\sum_{r=0}^{n} c_r^{\,2} = \frac{(2n)!}{(n!)^2}.$$

*23 Prove that $a + b^2 = 1$ is a necessary condition for one root of the equation $x^3 + ax + b = 0$ to be the reciprocal of another root. Show that the condition is also a sufficient one.

*24 Given that $p, q, r, s \in \mathbb{R}$, prove that $(pq + rs)^2 \leqslant (p^2 + r^2)(q^2 + s^2)$. Deduce that

$$(pqt + rsv)^2 \leqslant (p^2 + r^2)(q^2 + s^2)(t^2 + v^2),$$

where $t, v \in \mathbb{R}$.

25 Show that, for all values of θ,

$$(\cos\theta + 3\sin\theta)^2 \leqslant 10.$$

26 Given that $p, q \in \mathbb{R}^+$, show that the equation $x^3 - 3px^2 + 4q = 0$ has three distinct, real roots iff $p^3 > q$.

27 Given that $n \in \mathbb{Z}^+$, prove that
  (i) $2^{n+1} + 3^{2n-1} \equiv 0$ (modulo 7),
  (ii) $3^{2n} + 7 \equiv 0$ (modulo 8),
  (iii) $7^{2n} - 5 \times 7^n - 2 \equiv 0$ (modulo 6).

*28 Show that, when $\theta \neq 2k\pi$ for integer k,

$$\sum_{r=1}^{n} \cos r\theta = \frac{\cos\theta + \cos n\theta - \cos(n+1)\theta - 1}{2(1 - \cos\theta)}$$

$$= \frac{\sin(n\theta/2)\cos[(n+1)\theta/2]}{\sin(\theta/2)}.$$

Hence find $\sum_{r=1}^{n} \cos^2 r\theta$.

29 (a) Prove that

  (i) $\displaystyle\sum_{r=1}^{n} r = \frac{1}{2}n(n + 1),$

(ii) $\sum_{r=1}^{n} r(r+1) = \frac{1}{3}n(n+1)(n+2)$,

(iii) $\sum_{r=1}^{n} r^2 = \frac{1}{6}n(n+1)(2n+1)$.

(b) A game for two players, Alec and Bill, has the following rules. Alec throws two dice and Bill throws a third die. If either of Alec's dice show a higher number than Bill's die, Alec wins; otherwise Bill wins. Obtain the number of different ways in which the dice can fall and find the number of ways in which Bill wins.

In a modification of the game in which neither player wins when Alec's two dice show the same number, Bill can win in b ways and Alec can win in a ways. Calculate a and b.

30 Each of five towns, A, B, C, D, E, enters a team for a competition in each of seven events. A *result* of the competition consists of a table giving the town gaining first and second places in each event. (There are no ties.) Find the number of possible different results.

Calculate the number of possible results in which town A wins exactly one event, B is second in exactly one event and all the other first and second places are taken by the remaining three towns. (Leave your answers in a factorised form.)

31 Which one of the statements (b), (c), (d) concerning the sequence of real terms u_1, $u_2, \ldots, u_n, \ldots$ is the negation of statement (a)?
(a) $u_n < n$ for all positive integers n.
(b) $u_n \geqslant n$ for all positive integers n.
(c) $u_n \geqslant n$ for at least one positive integer n.
(d) $u_n < n$ for no positive integers n.
Consider now the statement (e):
(e) $u_1 = 0$ and for $n \geqslant 1$, $u_{n+1} < u_n + 1$.
Prove that (e) $\Rightarrow$ (a) and show by a counter-example that (a) $\not\Rightarrow$ (e).

32 Given that a, b, c, $d \in \mathbb{R}$, show that a necessary and sufficient condition that the simultaneous equations

$$ax + by = 2,$$

$$cx + dy = 3,$$

should have a unique solution for (x, y), is that the matrix $\mathbf{M}$, where $\mathbf{M} = \begin{pmatrix} a & b \\ c & d \end{pmatrix}$, should be non-singular.

In the case when $\mathbf{M}$ is singular, find the conditions that the number of solutions should be infinite.

33 Which of the following is (are) the converse of $(p \Rightarrow \sim q)$?
(a) $\sim p \Rightarrow q$
(b) $\sim p \Rightarrow \sim q$
(c) $p \Rightarrow q$
(d) $\sim q \Rightarrow p$
(e) $q \Rightarrow \sim p$

6   Some common fallacies and errors

In this chapter we give examples of common mistakes and misconceptions frequently made by students when writing out proofs. In particular, we discuss the examples of chapter 5. However, first we mention some of the more glaring errors and faults which occur far too regularly in examination scripts.

(i) Think before you write. Students misread questions, or rush in and solve enormous equations, or carry out prodigious manipulations which have little or nothing to do with the problem in hand.

(ii) Use all the data but do not assume facts which are not given. Proof of propositions must be as general as possible. Special cases are usually unrewarded! In Applied questions it is sometimes possible to have data supplied in the first sentence which are only used for later parts of the question, e.g. where the mass of a body is given and is only needed when the body is moving on an incline.

(iii) Distinguish carefully between equations and inequalities. The rules for manipulating inequalities are far stricter than those for equations (equalities).

(iv) When you use a calculator, you can retain additional decimal places as 'guard figures' but, in general, the accuracy required is specified. Keep to the specification. For example, if you have used the result $(1 + x)^{1/2} \approx 1 + x/2$ when x^2 is neglected, do not retain terms in x^2 in future work.

There are many snares for the unwary in the use of calculators. In Applied questions, particularly, premature evaluation of expressions occurring should always be avoided as this often masks the type of expression found and prevents cancelling and reduction to a much simpler form.

Calculators can also lead to an approximate answer being given when an exact one is wanted. If the answer to a question is ln 2 exactly, then there is little point in writing 0·693 unless asked to do so.

Again, if during the course of working out a problem you have used $g \approx 10\,\mathrm{m\,s^{-2}}$, or even $g \approx 9·8\,\mathrm{m\,s^{-2}}$, an answer such as 2·985 N is clearly absurd. The degree of accuracy required in numerical problems is usually stated, but, if this is not the case, then care should be taken that the approximation used is consistent with the data and should be clearly stated.

One common source of error in numerical solutions is premature approximation. Students should realise that an early correction to one decimal place can mean a grossly distorted result at the end of a long question.

A technical fault which can be due to the use of calculators is the confusion of degrees and radians when dealing with trigonometrical expressions.

Generally speaking, it is advisable to keep to radians so that numerical values for terms such as $\cos(\pi/10)$ can be found immediately.

(v) Be careful when squaring both sides of an equation. You can introduce additional roots.

Example 1   Consider the equation

$$\sqrt{(x^2 + 1)} = 2x - 1.$$

Squaring gives

$$(x^2 + 1 = 4x^2 - 4x + 1) \quad \Leftrightarrow \quad (3x^2 - 4x = 0)$$

$$\Leftrightarrow \quad (x = 0 \text{ or } x = 4/3).$$

Checking, we find that $x = 4/3$ satisfies the given equation but that $x = 0$ does not. In fact, $x = 0$ is a root of the equation

$$-\sqrt{(x^2 + 1)} = 2x - 1.$$

Example 2   As another example of the pitfalls of 'squaring both sides' consider the equation

$$(\cos x - \sin x = 1) \quad \Rightarrow \quad (\cos^2 x - 2 \sin x \cos x + \sin^2 x = 1)$$

$$\Leftrightarrow \quad (\sin 2x = 0)$$

$$\Leftrightarrow \quad (2x = n\pi \text{ for some } n \in \mathbb{Z})$$

$$\Leftrightarrow \quad (x = n\pi/2 \text{ for some } n \in \mathbb{Z}).$$

This is an attractively easy solution, but includes all the solutions of

$$\cos x - \sin x = -1$$

and hence is invalid. This can still be worth doing if only a limited range of values is wanted as it is easy to discard the invalid ones, otherwise it is better to use orthodox methods, e.g. $\cos(x + \pi/4) = 1/\sqrt{2}$ etc.

The following are comments on common errors which can arise in the examples of chapter 5. [The example numbers are those of chapter 5.]

*Example 1   No proof for special cases is acceptable. The proposition is true in general. A proof for particular matrices in no way answers the question.

*Example 2   An equivalent proof is

$$\cosh(x + y) - (\cosh x \cosh y + \sinh x \sinh y)$$

$$\equiv \tfrac{1}{2}(e^{x+y} + e^{-x-y}) - \tfrac{1}{2}(e^x + e^{-x}) \cdot \tfrac{1}{2}(e^y + e^{-y}) - \tfrac{1}{2}(e^x - e^{-x}) \cdot \tfrac{1}{2}(e^y - e^{-y})$$

$$\equiv \tfrac{1}{2}e^{x+y} + \tfrac{1}{2}e^{-x-y} - \tfrac{1}{4}e^{x+y} - \tfrac{1}{4}e^{-x+y} - \tfrac{1}{4}e^{x-y} - \tfrac{1}{4}e^{-x-y} - \tfrac{1}{4}e^{x+y} + \tfrac{1}{4}e^{x-y} +$$

$$\tfrac{1}{4}e^{-x+y} - \tfrac{1}{4}e^{-x-y}$$

$$\equiv 0.$$

But the following is a spurious proof

$$[\cosh(x+y) \equiv \cosh x \cosh y + \sinh x \sinh y]$$

$\Rightarrow \quad [\tfrac{1}{2}(e^{x+y} + e^{-x-y}) \equiv \tfrac{1}{2}(e^x + e^{-x})\tfrac{1}{2}(e^y + e^{-y}) + \tfrac{1}{2}(e^x - e^{-x})\tfrac{1}{2}(e^y - e^{-y})]$

$\Rightarrow \quad [\tfrac{1}{2}e^{x+y} + \tfrac{1}{2}e^{-x-y} \equiv \tfrac{1}{4}e^{x+y} + \tfrac{1}{4}e^{-x+y} + \tfrac{1}{4}e^{x-y} + \tfrac{1}{4}e^{-x-y} + \tfrac{1}{4}e^{x+y} - \tfrac{1}{4}e^{x-y} - $
$\tfrac{1}{4}e^{-x+y} + \tfrac{1}{4}e^{-x-y}]$

$\Rightarrow \quad [\tfrac{1}{2}e^{x+y} + \tfrac{1}{2}e^{-x-y} \equiv \tfrac{1}{2}e^{x+y} + \tfrac{1}{2}e^{-x-y}]$

$\Rightarrow \quad [0 \equiv 0]$

and so the proposition is true.

This argument is wrong because we have assumed the result and 'proved' the result $0 = 0$ (true but of no value). What is needed is a reversal of the four implication signs and a final line:

'which is a true statement and so the proposition is true.'

Example 3 A *false* argument (again the invalid $0 = 0$ argument) is as follows:

$$[\sin^2\theta\cos^2\phi - \cos^2\theta\sin^2\phi = \sin^2\theta - \sin^2\phi]$$

$\Rightarrow \quad [\sin^2\theta(1 - \sin^2\phi) - (1 - \sin^2\theta)\sin^2\phi = \sin^2\theta - \sin^2\phi]$

$\Rightarrow \quad [\sin^2\theta - \sin^2\phi = \sin^2\theta - \sin^2\phi]$

$\Rightarrow \quad [0 = 0].$

Hence the proposition is true.

Example 4 The result of this example could be verified as follows:

$$\left(\frac{dy}{dx} = \frac{[x + \sqrt{(1 + x^2)}]^{1/2}}{2\sqrt{(1 + x^2)}}\right) \quad \text{(if you notice the cancellation)}$$

$$\Rightarrow \quad \left(\frac{d^2y}{dx^2} = \frac{[x + \sqrt{(1 + x^2)}]^{1/2}}{4(1 + x^2)} - \frac{x[x + \sqrt{(1 + x^2)}]^{1/2}}{2(1 + x^2)^{3/2}}\right)$$

(if you use the first result).

Then, when $y = [x + \sqrt{(1 + x^2)}]^{1/2}$,

$$(1 + x^2)\frac{d^2y}{dx^2} + x\frac{dy}{dx} - \frac{1}{4}y = \frac{1}{4}[x + \sqrt{(1 + x^2)}]^{1/2} - \frac{x[x + \sqrt{(1 + x^2)}]^{1/2}}{2\sqrt{(1 + x^2)}}$$

$$+ \frac{x[x + \sqrt{(1 + x^2)}]^{1/2}}{2\sqrt{(1 + x^2)}} - \frac{1}{4}[x + \sqrt{(1 + x^2)}]^{1/2}$$

$$= 0.$$

This is a correct proof but one which is very liable to involve manipulative errors.

Example 5 A *false* proof of (i) is

$$[a^2 + b^2 \geqslant 2ab]$$

$$\Rightarrow \quad [a^2 - 2ab + b^2 \geqslant 0]$$

$$\Rightarrow \quad [(a - b)^2 \geqslant 0], \quad \text{which is true.}$$

Here we have assumed the result required to be proved. The lines in this proof are similar to those of the correct proof but the implication signs needed are in the opposite direction.

Example 6 A very misleading method is to try specific values of *x*. You might be lucky and locate the correct solution set, but even then you will not have proved that you have obtained the complete solution set.

Very wrong is the following

$$\left[0 < \frac{x(2 + x)}{2x + 1} < 1 \right]$$

(a) $\quad \Rightarrow \quad [0 < x(2 + x) < 2x + 1]$

$\quad \Rightarrow \quad [0 < x(2 + x) \text{ and } (x + 1)(x - 1) < 0]$

$\quad \Rightarrow \quad [x < -2 \text{ or } x > 0, \text{ and } -1 < x < 1]$

$\quad \Rightarrow \quad [\text{solution set is } \{x : 0 < x < 1\}].$

The 'solution' is of no value because, at line (a) we have multiplied by $(2x + 1)$ without considering whether it is positive or not.

However, we could have multiplied by $(2x + 1)^2$ which is positive (the function being undefined when $2x + 1 = 0$) and proceeded correctly as shown in chapter 5.

Solving inequalities or equalities requires arguments in both directions.

Example 7 An unwise method would be to write the equation as

$$\sin \theta = 1 - 2 \cos \theta,$$

then square and use $\sin^2 \theta = 1 - \cos^2 \theta$, thus

$$[\sin^2 \theta = (1 - 2 \cos \theta)^2]$$

$$\Rightarrow \quad [1 - \cos^2 \theta = 1 - 4 \cos \theta + 4 \cos^2 \theta]$$

$$\Rightarrow \quad [5 \cos^2 \theta - 4 \cos \theta = 0]$$

$$\Rightarrow \quad [\cos \theta (\cos \theta - 4/5) = 0]$$

$$\Rightarrow \quad [\cos \theta = 0 \text{ or } \cos \theta = 4/5]$$

$$\Rightarrow \quad [\theta = (360n + 90)° \text{ or } (360n \pm 36 \cdot 87)°].$$

Here we have obtained extra roots $(360n + 36\cdot87)°$. These are roots of

$$-\sin\theta = 1 - 2\cos\theta$$

which is *not* the equation we have to solve.

When you square an equation of the form $f(x) = g(x)$ prior to solving it, you must check that all the solutions which you find are, in fact, solutions of $f(x) = g(x)$. Some may be solutions of the equation $f(x) = -g(x)$.

Example 8   Notice how all the inequality signs in the arguments go in the same direction.

  *Excessive manipulation is rarely required in problems concerning complex numbers and it should be remembered that the theory of complex numbers involves both algebra and trigonometry. For example, to factorise $z^{2n+1} - a^{2n+1}$, where $n \in \mathbb{N}$, $a \in \mathbb{R}$, we first solve the equation

$$z^{2n+1} - a^{2n+1} = 0 \tag{6.1}$$

or

$$(z/a)^{2n+1} = 1.$$

Thus, for $r = -n, -(n-1), \ldots, 0, 1, \ldots, n$,

$$[(z/a)^{2n+1} = e^{2r\pi i}]$$

$$\Rightarrow \quad [z/a = e^{2r\pi i/(2n+1)}]$$

$$\Rightarrow \quad [z = ae^{2r\pi i/(2n+1)}].$$

The roots of (6.1) are therefore

$$z = a, \quad ae^{2ri\pi/(2n+1)}, \quad ae^{-2ri\pi/(2n+1)} \qquad (r = 1, 2, \ldots, n).$$

Therefore, by the factor theorem,

$$z^{2n+1} - a^{2n+1} = A(z - a) \prod_{r=1}^{n} (z - ae^{2ri\pi/(2n+1)})(z - ae^{-2ri\pi/(2n+1)})$$

$$= A(z - a) \prod_{r=1}^{n} (z^2 - 2az \cos[2r\pi/(2n+1)] + a^2).$$

Comparing coefficients of z^{2n+1} we find $A = 1$.

  Example 9   Some students may try the problem as follows:

$$\left[I_n = \int_0^x \frac{\mathrm{d}}{\mathrm{d}t}\left(\frac{t^{n+1}}{n+1}\right) \cos t\,\mathrm{d}t \right.$$

$$= \frac{x^{n+1}}{n+1}\cos x + \frac{1}{n+1}\int_0^x t^{n+1}\sin t\,\mathrm{d}t$$

$$= \frac{x^{n+1}}{n+1}\cos x + \frac{1}{n+1}\int_0^x \frac{\mathrm{d}}{\mathrm{d}t}\left(\frac{t^{n+2}}{n+2}\right)\sin t\,\mathrm{d}t$$

$$= \frac{x^{n+1}}{n+1}\cos x + \frac{x^{n+2}}{(n+1)(n+2)}\sin x - \frac{1}{(n+1)(n+2)}\int_0^x t^{n+2}\cos t\,dt \Bigg]$$

$$\Rightarrow \Bigg[\int_0^x t^{n+2}\cos t\,dt = x^{n+2}\sin x + (n+2)x^{n+1}\cos x - (n+2)(n+1)I_n \Bigg].$$

(6.2)

They then (or even sooner) despair and give up. But the required result is, in fact, within their grasp. All that is needed is to replace n by $n-2$ in equation (6.2) and the result follows at once. Recognising that proof of the proposition has, in fact, been accomplished is an important aspect of mathematics. Frequently, correct analysis is followed by much irrelevant (whether correct or incorrect) work.

Carelessness with signs is common in work of this kind. Checking each line (by backward differentiation) is useful.

Postscript

We have not presented any examples indicating the contortions gone through in searching for a proof by good or bad mathematicians. Many unhelpful directions are pursued, many mistakes are made, many hopeful intermediate conjectures turn out to be false, before a proof is found. A chain of implications to prove $P \Rightarrow Q$, say $P \Rightarrow P_1 \Rightarrow P_2 \Rightarrow Q$ is only as good as its weakest link, so that, if two implications turn out to be correct and one to be false, we get no proof of $P \Rightarrow Q$. Even the difficulty of recalling a proof reflects, to some extent, the unlikely and curious directions that proofs take. It is no wonder that students find proof difficult, but we thought that it would be unhelpful, even counterproductive, to present an example of various false starts before a correct proof is found. Suffice it to say that it is a time-consuming, sometimes exasperating, process that nobody finds easy.

Exercise 6

Explain what is wrong with each of the following 'proofs':
1   Suppose $x < y$. Then $1/x > 1/y$. Putting $x = -2$ and $y = 3$, we deduce that $-\frac{1}{2} > \frac{1}{3}$.
2   For all x, we have

$$\tan(180° - x) = -\tan x.$$

Taking $x = 90°$ we get

$$\tan(180° - 90°) = -\tan 90°.$$

That is $\tan 90° = -\tan 90°$ so that $\tan 90° = 0$.
3   Let $S = 1 + 2 + 4 + 8 + 16 + \dots$.
Then $2S = 2 + 4 + 8 + 16 + 32 + \dots = S - 1$
and so $S = -1$.

4   $\displaystyle \int_{-2}^{1} \frac{1}{x^2}\,dx = \left[-\frac{1}{x} \right]_{-2}^{1} = -1 - \left(-\frac{1}{2} \right) = -\frac{1}{2}.$

*5
$$\left[S = \sum_{r=1}^{\infty} 1/r, \ T = \sum_{r=1}^{\infty} (-1)^r/r \right]$$

$$\Rightarrow \left(S + T = \sum_{r=1}^{\infty} \frac{1}{r}[1 + (-1)^r] = \sum_{r=1}^{\infty} 2/(2r) = S \right)$$

$$\Rightarrow (T = 0).$$

However, $T = -\ln 2$ so that $\ln 2 = \ln 1$ or $2 = 1$.

*6
$$I = \int \frac{1}{t} dt = t \cdot \frac{1}{t} - \int \frac{t(-1)}{t^2} dt \qquad u = 1/t, \frac{dv}{dt} = 1,$$

$$= 1 + I \qquad\qquad\qquad \frac{du}{dt} = -1/t^2, v = t.$$

Hence $0 = 1$.

*7
$$\int \cot nx \, dx = \int \sin nx \frac{d}{dx}\left(\frac{-1}{n \sin nx}\right) dx$$

$$= \left[\frac{-1}{n \sin nx} \cdot \sin nx \right] + \int \frac{n \cos nx}{n \sin nx} dx$$

$$= -\frac{1}{n} + I_n.$$

Hence $\dfrac{1}{n} = 0 \quad \forall n.$

*8 What is wrong with the following argument?
We wish to prove

$P(n)$: If n people sit an exam, then they all get the same mark.

Proof by induction:
(i) $P(1)$ is true. If 1 person sits an exam then he scores his own mark.
(ii) $P(n) \Rightarrow P(n + 1)$. Suppose $(n + 1)$ people sit an exam. Then the first n constitute n people sitting the examination and so, by the induction hypothesis, they all score the same mark, say a. Moreover, the group 2, 3, ..., $(n + 1)$ also constitute n people sitting the exam and so they all score the same mark, say b. However, candidate 2 is common to both groups and so $a = b$, and all $(n + 1)$ people score the same mark.

7 Multiple choice examples

7.1 Relationship analysis

The questions of this section are examples of the relationship analysis multiple choice items used in some A-level examinations.

Each of these questions consists of two statements (in some cases following very brief preliminary information). You are required to determine the relationship between these statements and to choose:

			Directions summarised	
A	if **1** always implies **2** but **2** does not imply **1**		A	$1 \Rightarrow 2, 2 \not\Rightarrow 1$
B	if **2** always implies **1** but **1** does not imply **2**		B	$2 \Rightarrow 1, 1 \not\Rightarrow 2$
C	if **1** always implies **2** and **2** always implies **1**		C	$1 \Leftrightarrow 2$
D	if **1** always denies **2** and **2** always denies **1**		D	1 denies **2**, **2** denies 1
E	if none of the above relationships holds		E	None of these

We now give examples of simple relationships between real numbers to illustrate each of these responses.

A   **1** $x = 3$
          2 $x > 2$

As $3 > 2$ it is clear that **1** implies **2**, i.e. that **1** is a sufficient condition for **2**, but if $x > 2$ it does not follow that $x = 3$, i.e. **2** does not imply **1**. Hence key **A**. (The correct response to a multiple choice question is called its key.)

B If we reverse statements **1** and **2** in the example given then we get key **B**.

C   **1** $x^2 < 1$
          2 $-1 < x < 1$

In this example **1** is a necessary and sufficient condition for **2** and vice versa, i.e. $\{x : -1 < x < 1\}$ is the complete solution set of the inequality $x^2 < 1$. Hence the key is **C**.

D   **1** $x < 1$
          2 $x > 3$

In this example if $x < 1$ then x cannot be > 3 so that **1** always denies **2** and, likewise, **2** denies **1**. Hence the key is **D**.

E   **1** $x < 3$
          2 $x > 1$

In this example there is no implication relationship between the statements. If $x < 3$ it *could* be > 1, e.g. $x = 2$, but it need not necessarily be so, e.g. $x = -1$, so **1** neither implies nor denies **2** and, likewise, **2** neither implies nor denies **1**. Hence the key is **E**.

Exercise 7.1

Questions **1–28** are of single-subject A-level standard.

1 **1** $\sin x = 1/\sqrt{2}$
      2 $\tan x = 1$
2 **a** and **b** are non-zero vectors.
      1 $|\mathbf{a}| = |\mathbf{b}|$
      2 $\mathbf{a} = \mathbf{b}$
3 **1** f(x) is an odd function
      2 $\displaystyle\int_{-1}^{1} f(x)\,dx = 0$
4 **1** The curve $y = f(x)$ has an inflexion when $x = a$
      2 $f''(a) = 0$
5 **1** f: $x \mapsto \ln(1 + x)$
      2 $f^{-1} : x \mapsto e^{(x-1)}$
6 **1** f(x) has a maximum when $x = a$
      2 $f'(a) = 0,\ f''(a) < 0$

7 **1** $\displaystyle\sum_{r=0}^{\infty} (3e^{-x})^r = 4$
      2 $x = \ln 4$
8 **1** $\sin x = \sin 2x$
      2 $x = n\pi$, where $n \in \mathbb{Z}$
9 f(x) ≡ $x^3 - 3p^2x + 2$, where $p > 0$.
      1 The equation f(x) = 0 has three real roots
      2 $p < 1$
10 **1** $\sin x = 1/2$
       2 $\cos x = (\sqrt{3})/2$
11 **1** The series $\displaystyle\sum_{r=1}^{\infty} ar^n$ converges
       2 $|a| < 1$
12 **1** f(x) = $x/(1 + x^2)$
       2 $\displaystyle\int_{2}^{3} f(x)\,dx = \tfrac{1}{2}\ln 2$
13 **1** f(x) = 2^x
       2 $f'(x) = 2^x/(\ln 2)$

14 1 $\sin(x - y) = \sin(x + y)$ for all $x \in \mathbb{R}$

2 $y = 2n\pi$, where $n \in \mathbb{Z}$

15 z is a complex number.

1 $|z - 1| = |z + 3|$

2 The locus of z in the Argand diagram is the line $\operatorname{Re} z = -1$

16 1 $\displaystyle\int_a^b f(x)\,dx = k$

2 $\displaystyle\int_a^b \frac{1}{f(x)}\,dx = \frac{1}{k}$

17 $\mathbf{a}$ and $\mathbf{b}$ are non-zero vectors.

1 $|\mathbf{a}| = |\mathbf{b}|$

2 The vectors $(\mathbf{a} + \mathbf{b})$ and $(\mathbf{a} - \mathbf{b})$ are perpendicular

18 1 $|x| > 1$

2 $x > 2$

19 1 $\cos\theta° = \cos 420°$

2 $\theta = 360n + 60$ for $n \in \mathbb{Z}$

20 1 $f(x) = \ln(x^4)$

2 $f'(x) = 4/x^5$

21 z_1 and z_2 are non-zero complex numbers.

1 $z_1 z_2$ is real

2 $\arg(z_1 z_2) = \pi$

22 1 The equation $3\sin\theta + 4\cos\theta = k$ has two different solutions in the range $0 \leqslant \theta < 360$

2 $|k| < 5$

23 1 $\dfrac{dy}{dx} = x$

2 $\dfrac{d^2 x}{dy^2} = \dfrac{-1}{x^3}$

24 1 $\dfrac{1}{\alpha} + \dfrac{1}{\beta} = \dfrac{1}{2}$

2 α and β are the roots of the equation $x^2 - 2x + 4 = 0$

25 1 The straight lines $x - 2y + 3 = 0$, $2x + y - 5 = 0$ and $3x - y + k = 0$ are concurrent

2 $k = 8$

26 1 $y = 3x^2 - 2/x$

2 If xy is plotted against x^3 the points lie on a straight line

27 z is a complex number.

1 $\operatorname{Re} z = \operatorname{Im} z$

2 $|z| = 1$

28 1 $1 < x < 2$

2 $|x - 1| < |x - 2|$

*Questions **29–56** are of double-subject (or pure mathematics) A-level standard.

29 1 $\cosh x = \sqrt{2}$

2 $\sinh x = 1$

30 $\mathbf{A}$, $\mathbf{B}$ and $\mathbf{C}$ are non-singular $n \times n$ matrices.

1 $\mathbf{A} = \mathbf{BC}$

2 $\mathbf{A}^{-1} = \mathbf{C}^{-1}\mathbf{B}^{-1}$

31 1 $\dfrac{d^2 y}{dx^2} + 2\dfrac{dy}{dx} + 5y = 0$

2 $y = e^x(P\cos 2x + Q\sin 2x)$, where P, Q are arbitrary constants

32 $\mathbf{a}$, $\mathbf{b}$, $\mathbf{c}$ and $\mathbf{x}$ are non-zero vectors.

1 $\mathbf{a} + \mathbf{b} = \mathbf{c}$

2 $\mathbf{a} \times \mathbf{x} + \mathbf{b} \times \mathbf{x} = \mathbf{c} \times \mathbf{x} \quad \forall \mathbf{x}$

33 1 $f(xy) = f(x) + f(y) \quad \forall x, y \in \mathbb{R}$

2 $f(x + y) = f(x) \cdot f(y) \quad \forall x, y \in \mathbb{R}$

34 1 $\mathbf{X}$ is a 4×3 matrix

2 $\mathbf{X}^T\mathbf{X}$ is a 3×3 matrix

35 $\mathbf{p}$ and $\mathbf{q}$ are non-zero vectors.

1 $\mathbf{p} \cdot \mathbf{q} \neq 0$

2 $\mathbf{p} \times \mathbf{q} = \mathbf{0}$

36 n is a non-zero constant.

1 $\dfrac{d^2 y}{dt^2} = -n^2 y$

2 $y = P\cos nt + Q\sin nt$, P and Q being arbitrary constants

37 1 $z = e^{2\pi i/n}$, where $n \in \mathbb{Z}^+$

2 $z^n = 1$

38 z is a complex number.

1 $|z + 1| < |z - 1|$

2 $|z + i| < |z - i|$

39 1 The series $\displaystyle\sum_{r=1}^{\infty} r(x/2)^r$ is convergent

2 $|x| < 2$

40 1 $p \Rightarrow q$

2 $q \Rightarrow p$

41 1 $p \Rightarrow q$

2 $\sim p \Rightarrow \sim q$

42 1 $f(x)$ is continuous in the interval $[a, b]$ and $f(a) \cdot f(b) < 0$

2 The equation $f(x) = 0$ has at least one root in the interval $[a, b]$

43 1 $\dfrac{x(x - 2)}{1 - x} > 0$

2 $2 > x > 1$

44 $f(z) = az^3 + bz + c$, where $a, b, c \in \mathbb{R}$.

1 $(1 - 2i)$ is a root of $f(z) = 0$

2 $(-1 + 2i)$ is a root of $f(z) = 0$

45 **a** is a non-zero scalar and **P** is an arbitrary vector.

1 $\dfrac{d\mathbf{r}}{dt} + a\mathbf{r} = \mathbf{0}$

2 $\mathbf{r} = \mathbf{P}e^{at}$

46 $a, b \in \mathbb{R}$ and $ab \neq 0$.

1 $a > b$

2 $1/a < 1/b$

47 z_1 and z_2 are complex numbers.

1 $|z_1| - |z_2| < 2$

2 $|z_1 - z_2| < 2$

48 $f(x)$ is a cubic polynomial in x.

1 The equation $f(x) = 0$ has a repeated root $x = a$

2 $f(a) = 0$, $f'(a) = 0$

49 1 $f'(x) > g'(x)$ for $a \leqslant x \leqslant b$

2 $f(x) > g(x)$ for $a \leqslant x \leqslant b$

50 1 $\dfrac{dy}{dx} + 2y = 3$

2 $\dfrac{d^2y}{dx^2} + 4\dfrac{dy}{dx} + 4y = 9$

51 1 $\tanh(x/2) = \frac{1}{3}$

2 $\tanh x = \frac{2}{3}$

52 1 $p \Rightarrow q$

2 $\sim q \Rightarrow \sim p$

53 1 The non-zero solutions of the differential equation $\dfrac{d^2y}{dx^2} = ky$, where k is a constant, are all periodic

2 $k > 0$

54 1 α, β and γ are the roots of the equation

$$x^3 + 2x^2 - 3x + 7 = 0$$

2 $\alpha^2 + \beta^2 + \gamma^2 = 10$

55 1 $f(x)$ is a continuous function of x for $a \leqslant x \leqslant b$

2 $f'(x)$ is a continuous function of x for $a \leqslant x \leqslant b$

56 1 $\sin mx + \sin nx$, where m, n are constants is a periodic function of x

2 $m/n \in \mathbb{Q}$

7.2 Data sufficiency

The questions of this section are examples of the data sufficiency multiple-choice items used in some A-level examinations.

Each of the questions consists of a problem and two statements, **1** and **2**, in which certain data are given. You are not asked to solve the problem: you have to decide whether the data given in the statements are sufficient for solving the problem. Using the data given in the statements, choose

A if each statement (i.e. statement **1** *alone* and statement **2** *alone*) is sufficient by itself to solve the problem

B if statement **1** *alone* is sufficient but statement **2** alone is not sufficient to solve the problem

C if statement **2** *alone* is sufficient but statement **1** alone is not sufficient to solve the problem

D if *both* statements **1** and **2** *together* are sufficient to solve the problem, but *neither* statement *alone* is sufficient

E if statements **1** and **2** *together* are *not* sufficient to solve the problem, and additional data specific to the problem are needed.

Directions summarised	
A	Either
B	**1**
C	**2**
D	Both
E	Neither

Exercise 7.2

Questions **1–28** are of single-subject A-level standard.

1 Find the value of $\cos x$.
  1 $\sin x = 1/\sqrt{2}$
  2 $\tan x = -1$

2 $f(z) = z^3 + pz^2 + qz - 10$, where $p, q \in \mathbb{R}$. Find the values of p and q.
  1 2 is a root of the equation $f(z) = 0$
  2 $1 - 2i$ is a root of the equation $f(z) = 0$

3 Prove that $x^2 + 2bx + c > 0$ for all $x \in \mathbb{R}$.
  1 $b^2 < c$
  2 $c > 0$

4 Show that the equation $f(x) = 0$ has a double root a.
  1 $f(a) = 0$
  2 $f'(a) = 0$

5 Prove that $\sin(x + n\pi) < 0$.
  1 $\pi < x < 3\pi/2$
  2 $n \in \mathbb{Z}$

6 Prove that $(x - 1)^2(y + 1)^3 \geqslant 0$, where $x, y \in \mathbb{R}$.
  1 $x > 1$
  2 $y > -1$

7 Given that $\dfrac{dy}{dx} = y \tan x$, find the value of y when $x = \pi/3$.
  1 $y = 1$ when $x = 0$
  2 $y = -1$ when $x = \pi$

8 The first term of a geometric progression of positive terms is 8. Find the sum to infinity.
  1 The sum of the first three terms is 14
  2 The fourth term is equal to 1

9 Prove that $\displaystyle\int_0^2 f(x)\,dx > 2$.
  1 $f'(x) > 1$ for $0 \leqslant x \leqslant 2$
  2 $f(x) > x$ for $0 \leqslant x \leqslant 2$

10 Show that $f(1) > f(0)$.
  1 $f(x) > x$ for $0 \leqslant x \leqslant 1$
  2 $f'(x) > x$ for $0 \leqslant x < 1$

. 11 $f(x) = x^3 + px^2 + q$.
Find the values of p and q.
  1 $f(x)$ has a maximum value 5 when $x = -2$
  2 $f(x)$ has a minimum value 1 when $x = 0$

12 Find the sum of the first 100 terms of the arithmetic progression whose first term is -195.
  1 The one hundredth term is 300
  2 The common difference is 5

13 Find an equation of the circle with centre C which cuts the x-axis at the point K.
  1 $OC = 13$
  2 K is the point $(12, 0)$

14 Show that $\dfrac{a + bi}{1 + i}$ is a real number, where $a, b \in \mathbb{Z}$.
  1 $a = b$
  2 $a = 2$

15 Find the rate of increase, with respect to time, of the volume of a sphere at a given instant.
  1 The rate of increase, with respect to time, of the surface area at the given instant is given
  2 The rate of increase, with respect to time, of the radius at the given instant is given

16 Find, approximately, the percentage increase in the volume of a right circular cone of constant base radius.
  1 The base radius of the cone is given
  2 The small percentage increase in the height of the cone is given

17 Show that both the roots of the equation $ax^2 + bx + c = 0$, where a, b, c are positive.
  1 $ab < 0$
  2 $ac > 0$

18 Find the value of the parameter t corresponding to the point P which is the foot of the perpendicular from the origin O to the straight line with vector equation $\mathbf{r} = \mathbf{a} + t\mathbf{b}$.
  1 $\mathbf{a} \cdot \mathbf{b}$ is given
  2 $\mathbf{b} \cdot \mathbf{b}$ is given

19 Show that the curve $y = f(x)$ has a point of inflexion when $x = a$.
  1 $f'(a) = 0$
  2 $f''(a) = 0$

20 Show that the equation $f(x) = 0$, where $f(x)$ is a polynomial in x of degree n, has just one real root.
1 $f'(x) > 0$ for all x
2 n is odd

21 Find the angles of the triangle PQR.
1 $\overrightarrow{PQ} . \overrightarrow{PR}$ and $\overrightarrow{PR} . \overrightarrow{RQ}$ are given
2 $\overrightarrow{PQ}$ and $\overrightarrow{PR}$ are given

22 Prove that $|x - 1| > |x + 1|$.
1 $|x| < 1$
2 $x < 0$

23 α and β are the real roots of the equation $x^2 + px + q = 0$. Show that $\alpha^3 + \beta^3 > 0$.
1 $p < 0$
2 $q > 0$

24 Show that the equation $e^x = k \cos ax$, where a and k are constants, has no positive roots.
1 $a > 0$
2 $k < 1$

25 $x \neq (2n + 1)\pi/2$, where $n \in \mathbb{Z}$. Prove that $\tan^2 x > 1$.
1 $\sin x > 1/\sqrt{2}$
2 $\cos x < 1/\sqrt{2}$

26 Expand $\dfrac{1}{(a - x)(b - x)}$, where $a, b \in \mathbb{R}^+$, in ascending powers of x.
1 $|x| < a$
2 $a < b$

27 Find the period of the function $a \sin kx + b \cos kx$.
1 $k = 1/5$
2 $a = b = 2$

28 a is a positive constant. Prove that $|x| \leqslant 2a$.
1 $x^2 + y^2 \leqslant a^2$
2 $|x - a| + |y - a| \leqslant a$

*Questions 29–58 are of double-subject (or pure mathematics) A-level standard.

29 Show that $\sinh x > 1$.
1 $\cosh x > \sqrt{2}$
2 $\tanh x > 1/\sqrt{2}$

30 Given that $\dfrac{d^2y}{dx^2} = -4y$ and $y = 0$ when $x = 0$, find the value of y when $x = \pi/8$.
1 When $x = \pi/2$, $y = 0$
2 When $x = \pi/4$, $y = 2$

31 Prove that the proposition p is true.
1 $\sim p \Rightarrow r$, and r is false
2 $p \Rightarrow q$ and q is true

32 Show that the series $\displaystyle\sum_{r=1}^{\infty} e^{-rx}/r^{\alpha}$ converges.
1 $\alpha > 1$
2 $x > 0$

33 Find the constants p and q in the differential equation
$$\frac{d^2y}{dx^2} + p\frac{dy}{dx} + qy = 5 - 6x.$$
1 The complementary function is $Pe^x + Qe^{-2x}$, P and Q being arbitrary constants
2 A particular integral is $3x - 1$

34 Prove that the series $\displaystyle\sum_{r=1}^{\infty} u_r$ converges.
1 $u_r < 1/r$
2 $u_r > 0$

35 Given that $\dfrac{d\mathbf{r}}{dt} = -2\mathbf{r}$, find $\mathbf{r}$ in terms of t.
1 $\mathbf{r} = 2\mathbf{i}$ when $t = 0$
2 $\dfrac{d\mathbf{r}}{dt} = -4\mathbf{i}$ when $t = 0$

36 Find the value of u_n.
1 $\displaystyle\sum_{r=1}^{n} u_r = n(2n - 1)$ for all $n \in \mathbb{Z}^+$
2 $u_r - u_{r-1} = 4$, for all $r \in \mathbb{Z}^+$

37 Prove that n is divisible by 9.
1 n^2 is divisible by 9
2 n^3 is odd

38 One root of the equation
$$ax^3 + bx^2 + bx + 1 = 0$$
is β. Prove that $1/\beta$ is also a root.
1 $a = 1$
2 $b = -1$

39 Find the polar equation of the locus of P.
1 The locus of P is a circle of radius a
2 The locus of P is a circle whose centre lies on the circle $r = a$

40 PQ is an arc of the curve whose polar equation is $r = e^{-2\theta}$, $0 \leqslant \theta \leqslant 2\pi$. Calculate the area of the sector OPQ, where O is the pole.
1 Angle OPQ is given
2 OP and OQ are given

41 Prove that

$$a^2 + b^2 + c^2 > ab + bc + ca,$$

where $a, b, c \in \mathbb{R}$.
1 $(a - b)(b - c)(c - a) \neq 0$
2 a, b and c are all positive

42 Show that the equation $\ln x = kx$ has just two real, distinct positive roots.
1 $k > 0$
2 $k < e^{-1}$

43 Referred to the origin O, the position vectors of the points P, Q, R are the non-zero vectors $\mathbf{p}, \mathbf{q}, \mathbf{r}$ respectively. Show that P, Q and R are colinear.
1 There exist non-zero constants λ, μ, ν such that

$$\lambda\mathbf{p} + \mu\mathbf{q} + \nu\mathbf{r} = \mathbf{0}$$

2 $\lambda + \mu + \nu = 0$

44 Given that $\dfrac{dy}{dx} + \dfrac{y}{x} = 3x$, find the value of y when $x = 2$.
1 When $x = 1, y = 1$
2 When $x = 1, \dfrac{dy}{dx} = 2$

45 Prove that the curve $y = \dfrac{kx}{x^2 - c}$, where $k \neq 0$, has just two turning points.
1 $k > 0$
2 $c < 0$

46 P, Q, R are non-singular $n \times n$ matrices. Find $(\mathbf{PQR})^{-1}$.
1 $\mathbf{R}^{-1}$ and $\mathbf{Q}^{-1}\mathbf{P}^{-1}$ are given
2 $\mathbf{Q}^{-1}$ and $\mathbf{R}^{-1}\mathbf{P}^{-1}$ are given

47 Find the value of $\cosh x$.
1 $\sinh^{-1} x$ is given
2 $\tanh^{-1} x$ is given

48 Show that $p \Rightarrow q$.
1 $\sim p \Rightarrow \sim q$
2 $\sim q \Rightarrow \sim p$

49 Show that the series $\sum\limits_{r=1}^{\infty} u_r$ converges.
1 $u_n \to 0$ as $n \to \infty$
2 $u_n > 0$ for all n

50 Given that $\dfrac{d\mathbf{r}}{dt} = 2\mathbf{r} + t\mathbf{i}$, find $\mathbf{r}$ in terms of $\mathbf{i}, \mathbf{j}, \mathbf{k}$ and t.
1 $\mathbf{r} = \mathbf{j} - 2\mathbf{k}$ when $t = 0$
2 $d\mathbf{r}/dt = 2\mathbf{j} - 4\mathbf{k}$ when $t = 0$

51 Investigate whether the series of positive terms $\sum\limits_{r=1}^{\infty} u_r$ converges or diverges.
1 $u_r < re^{-r}$ for $r > 20\,000$
2 $u_r < 1/r^{3/2}$ for $r > 10\,000$

52 Given that $\mathbf{a}$ is a known non-zero vector, find $\mathbf{x}$.
1 $\mathbf{x} \times \mathbf{a}$ is given
2 $\mathbf{x} \cdot \mathbf{a}$ is given

53 Given that $f(x) \geqslant 0$ for $x \in \mathbb{R}^+$, show that the integral $\displaystyle\int_0^{\infty} f(x)\,dx$ converges.
1 $f(x) < e^{-x}$ for $x \geqslant 1$
2 $f(x) < 1/\sqrt{x}$ for $0 < x < 1$

54 z is a complex number. Prove that $\text{Re}(z^5) > 0$.
1 $0 < \arg z < \pi/2$
2 $\text{Im}(z^5) > 0$

55 Find the volume swept out when an equilateral triangle of side a is rotated through 2π radians about an axis in its plane.
1 The axis is parallel to a side of the triangle
2 The axis is at a distance a from the centroid of the triangle

56 Given that $\mathbf{b}$ is a non-zero vector, show that $\mathbf{a} = \mathbf{0}$.
1 $\mathbf{a} \times \mathbf{b} = \mathbf{0}$
2 $\mathbf{a} \cdot \mathbf{b} = 0$

57 Calculate $|z|$.
1 $|z - 2 - 3i| = 3$
2 $\arg(z - i) = \pi/4$

58 Show that the geometric series $\sum\limits_{r=1}^{\infty} \left(\dfrac{x}{x+1}\right)^r$ is convergent.
1 $x > -\frac{1}{2}$
2 $|x| < 1$

8 The use of English by mathematicians

[by Professor C. A. Rogers FRS]

English is a beautiful and precise language. However, in some ways, it is not exactly suited to the needs of mathematicians. Mathematicians have come to use English with a few peculiar conventions; some are so used to these peculiarities that they use them without recognition of their existence.

One of the most obvious ways in which mathematicians use English in a special way causes very little difficulty. We use common words like 'set', 'group', 'ring', 'field', 'number' in special technical ways. But it is usually quite clear from the context that the words are being used in the technical sense. After all, we are very used to the fact that we have to guess the meaning of words. If the farmer has a corn on his toe and a sow in his pigsty and goes to sow corn in his field, we understand.

Let me discuss the word 'or'. This is used in two distinct ways in normal English. If a highwayman cries 'Stand and deliver! Your money or your life!' one assumes that he means to take your money or your life but not both. Doubtless, if he takes your life he will also take your money, but this is not what he is saying. On the other hand, if someone advises you 'It is going to rain. I should take a raincoat or an umbrella', then he will not be unduly surprised if you take both. In the common use of English the 'exclusive or' with the meaning 'one or the other but not both' is the most frequent. In mathematics, the word 'or' is almost always used in the inclusive sense, meaning 'one or the other or both'. Thus when we define the union $A \cup B$ of the two sets A and B to be the set of all elements that are in A or B we mean the set of all elements that are in A or in B or in both A and B.

Again a mathematician will happily write $1 \leqslant 2$, or say 'One is less than or equal to two'. It is wrong to think that the statement 'One is less than or equal to two' is false. It is, of course, a statement that says less than it might say, as we all know that one is less than two and is not equal to two. Statements like 'one is less than or equal to two' often arise in disguised form in the course of mathematical argument. For example, we have

$$x + \frac{1}{x} \geqslant 2, \quad \text{for } x > 0.$$

We deduce, by substitution, that

$$1 + \frac{1}{y} + \frac{1}{1 + \frac{1}{y}} \geqslant 2, \quad \text{for } y > 0. \tag{8.1}$$

The fact that there is no y with $y > 0$ and

$$1 + \frac{1}{y} + \frac{1}{1 + \dfrac{1}{y}} = 2,$$

does not mean that the statement (8.1) is wrong; it merely means that (8.1) does not say quite as much as it might say. It is just as well that we do not always say as much as we might say.

The English language has many 'quantifiers', that is, words such as 'all', 'some', 'few', 'many', 'any' that answer the question 'How many?' In mathematics 'all' and 'some' are by far the most useful and 'any' is by far the most dangerous. In some contexts 'some' can be substituted for 'any' without change of meaning, in other contexts 'all' can be so substituted. If someone asks you 'Did you meet anyone when you came up the staircase?' he is asking if there was someone (but not someone in particular) on the stairs. However, if he says 'Any idiot would tell you that', he means that all idiots, if asked, would tell you. In other contexts, particularly in conditional clauses using the word 'if', the word 'any' becomes highly ambiguous. Suppose that $f: x \mapsto f(x)$ is a real-valued function defined for all real values of x. Consider the two statements (a) and (b):

(a) If $f(x) < 0$ for any real x, then there is no real-valued function g with

$$[g(x)]^2 = f(x),$$

for all real x.

(b) If $f(x) > 0$ for any real x, then there is a real-valued function g with

$$[g(x)]^2 = f(x),$$

for all real x.

The natural interpretation of (a) is that, as soon as there is some real value of x, say x_1, with $f(x_1) < 0$, then it is impossible to find a real-valued function g with

$$[g(x)]^2 = f(x)$$

as the existence of such a function g would give

$$0 \leqslant [g(x_1)]^2 = f(x_1) < 0.$$

I believe that the proper interpretation of (b) is similar, so that (b) is false, as the mere existence of some real x_1 with $f(x_1) > 0$ is not enough to ensure the existence of g in every case, since there may well be some other real number, x_2, say, with $f(x_2) < 0$. Nevertheless, there is a tremendous temptation to interpret (b) to mean that, for all real values of x we have $f(x) > 0$, so that the conclusion follows; and the statement becomes true, when interpreted in this way. If I had my way I would ban any use of the word 'any' in any mathematics.

Another source of difficulty is a method of classification that has been taken for granted throughout the period when English developed its present form. The very structure of the language includes the system of classification by dichotomy (literally 'cutting into two'). Thus we have distinctions between men and women, between man and animals, between birds and beasts. This contrasts with scientific classifications that use groups within groups. Thus Men and Women are regarded as subgroups of the Humans. Humans, Chimpanzees and Gorillas are subgroups of the Primates. Primates and the family of Cats are subgroups of the Mammals. Mammals and Fish are subgroups of the Vertebrates, and so on. Mathematicians use this inclusive type of classification. The natural numbers are a subset of the integers. The integers are a subset of the rational numbers. The rational numbers and the irrational numbers (here we do have a dichotomy) form subsets of the real numbers. The real numbers are a subset of the complex numbers. The complex numbers are a subset of the quaternions.

Although many may find no difficulty with these mathematical ways of using English, I have in my teaching of University students, repeatedly found them to be a source of difficulty that can be very easily overlooked.

Answers

Exercise 2.1

1 $p \Rightarrow q$

2 Yes

3 A

4 D

5 A

6 D

7 $p \Rightarrow q$

8 E

9 D

10 $AB \| DC$ and $AD \| BC$; $AB \| DC$ and $AB = DC$; $AB = DC$ and $AD = BC$; $\angle A = \angle C$ and $\angle B = \angle D$; AC and BD bisect each other.

Miscellaneous exercise 2

2 $a > 0, b^2 - 4ac < 0$

3 $\left(\dfrac{2e^x}{1 + e^x} < 1 \right) \Leftrightarrow (x < 0)$

7 $st = -1$

Exercise 3

1 Both false

2 $\Leftrightarrow$

3 $\Leftarrow$; $\begin{pmatrix} \frac{1}{2} & \frac{1}{2} \\ \frac{1}{2} & \frac{1}{2} \end{pmatrix}$

4 $\Rightarrow$; $\begin{pmatrix} 1 & 1 \\ 1 & 1 \end{pmatrix}\begin{pmatrix} 1 & -1 \\ -1 & 1 \end{pmatrix}$

5 $\Leftarrow$; kite

6 $\Leftrightarrow$

7 $\Leftrightarrow$

8 $\Rightarrow$; $f(x) = x^4$

9 $\Leftrightarrow$

10 $\Leftarrow$

11 $\Rightarrow$

12 False

13 Both false

14 $\Leftarrow$; $x = \sin \omega t$

15 $\Rightarrow$; $f = \sin, a = 0, b = 2\pi$

Exercise 4.1 (a)

1 (i) $\tanh(a/b)$ if $b \neq 0$; 1 if $b = 0, a > 0$; -1 if $b = 0, a < 0$; $\tanh 2$ if $b = 0, a = 0$.

(ii) $\tanh(c/d)$ if $d \neq 0$; $\tanh 2$ if $c = 0$, $d = 0$; 1 if $d = 0, c > 0$; -1 if $d = 0, c < 0$.

3 $k \neq l$, unique solution. $\left(\dfrac{kb - la}{k - l}, \dfrac{a - b}{k - l} \right)$, 2 intersecting lines; $k = l$, $a \neq b$, solution set empty, 2 parallel lines; $k = l$, $a = b$, solution set infinite, 2 coincident lines.

4 $a^2 = b$, $-(x + a)^{-1} + C$; $a^2 > b$,
$\dfrac{1}{2\sqrt{(a^2 - b)}} \ln\left(\dfrac{x + a - \sqrt{(a^2 - b)}}{x + a + \sqrt{(a^2 - b)}} \right) + C$;
$a^2 < b$, $\dfrac{1}{\sqrt{(b - a^2)}} \tan^{-1}\left(\dfrac{x + a}{\sqrt{(b - a^2)}} \right) + C$.

5 $a^2 = b$, $y = (Ax + B)e^{-ax}$;
$a^2 > b$, $y = A e^{[-a + \sqrt{(a^2 - b)}]x} + B e^{[-a - \sqrt{(a^2 - b)}]x}$;
$a^2 < b$, $y = e^{-ax}[A \cos(\sqrt{(b - a^2)}x) + B \sin(\sqrt{(b - a^2)}x)]$.

8 3 real roots if $a < 0$ and $b^2 < -4a^3$; 1 real root if $a > 0$ or if $a < 0$ and $b^2 > -4a^3$; 3 real roots with 2 coincident if $b^2 = -4a^3$.

9 (a) $(1, -2, 1)$, 3 planes intersect at one point; (b) Solution set empty, intersection lines of each pair of planes parallel; (c) Solution set infinite, 3 planes have a common line
$[x = t - \frac{1}{2}, y = \frac{3}{2} - 3t, z = t]$.

10 $k \neq 1$, unique solution, 3 planes intersect at one point; $k = 1$, $l = 1$, solution set infinite, 3 planes have line in common; $k = 1$, $l \neq 1$, solution set empty, planes intersect in lines which are parallel.

11 (i) $y = \dfrac{1}{a + b}e^{bx} + ce^{-ax}, a \neq -b$;
$y = C, a = b = 0$; $y = (x + C)e^{-ax}$, $a = -b \neq 0$;
(ii) $p \neq \pm n, y = A \cos nx + B \sin nx + (\cos px)/(n^2 - p^2)$;
$p = \pm n, y = A \cos nx + B \sin nx + \dfrac{x}{2n} \sin nx$.

12 $(pa+q)(pb+q) > 0$,
$\dfrac{1}{p}\ln\left|\dfrac{pb+q}{pa+q}\right|$.

Exercise 4.1(b)
3 $x = 0$
4 $\{x: -1 < x < \tfrac{1}{2}\}$
5 $(x-x_1)(x-x_2) + (y-y_1)(y-y_2) = 0$
6 $x = 2; \pm 2\sqrt{2}y = x - 6$
7 $(3,1)$
9 $k < 1, |\tfrac{1}{2} - \cos k\pi|; 1 \leqslant k \leqslant 2, (5/2 + \cos k\pi)$
10 $n < 0, x = Ae^{t\sqrt{-n}} + Be^{t\sqrt{-n}}; n = 0, x = At + B; n > 0, x = A\cos(t\sqrt{n}) + B\sin(t\sqrt{n})$
11 Locus is $(k^2-1)(x^2+y^2) - 2x(2k^2-1) + 4k^2 - 1 = 0$, circle when $k \neq 1$, straight line ($x = 3/2$) when $k = 1$
12 When $|a| < 2$, 3 real distinct roots; when $|a| = 2$, 3 real roots (2 coincident); when $|a| > 2$, 1 real root.
13 $\{x: -1 < x < 1\} \cup \{x: x > 2\}$

Exercise 4.3
2 $\{x: x > 0, x \neq 1\}$
3 $\{x: x < 0\} \cup \{x: x > 1\}$
4 $\{x: 1 < x < 5\}$

Exercise 4.4
4 $n = 4$

Exercise 4.5
3 $x\dfrac{dv}{dx} = \dfrac{1+v^2}{1-v}, \tan^{-1}\left(\dfrac{y}{x}\right) = \dfrac{1}{2}\ln(x^2 + y^2) + c$
6 $C + iS = \displaystyle\sum_{r=1}^{n} e^{ir\theta}$,
$\dfrac{\cos[(n+1)\theta/2]\sin(n\theta/2)}{\sin(\theta/2)}$;
$\dfrac{n\cos[(n+\frac{1}{2})\theta]}{2\sin(\theta/2)} - \dfrac{\sin n\theta}{4\sin^2(\theta/2)}, \theta \neq 2n\pi$
8 286

Exercise 4.6
10 e^x

Exercise 4.8
1 $a = 2, b = -4, c = 1, d = -1$
2 $x = -2$
3 $a = 1 = b$
4 $\begin{pmatrix} 1 & 2 \\ 3 & 4 \end{pmatrix}$ and $\begin{pmatrix} 2 & 1 \\ 4 & 3 \end{pmatrix}$

5 $f(x) = x$ for $x > 0$, $f(x) = 1 - x$ for $x \leqslant 0$
6 $x = \pi/3, y = 5\pi/6$
7 A is singular, e.g. $\begin{pmatrix} 1 & 1 \\ 1 & 1 \end{pmatrix}$
8 The magnitudes of the forces are proportional to the lengths of the sides $\Rightarrow$ a couple

Exercise 4.9
3 π
4 $\tfrac{1}{2}$

Exercise 5
2 $f(b) = f(c) = 0$. Hence $(x-b)(x-c)$ is a factor of $f(x)$
3 $7^{n+1} + 3^{n+1} + 6 = 7(7^n + 3^n + 6) - 4(3^n + 9); (3^n + 9)$ even
4 $5^{2n+2} + 3(n+1) - 1 = 25(5^{2n} + 3n - 1) - 9.8n + 9.3$
5 $\cos 2(n+1)\theta + \dfrac{[\sin(2n+1)\theta]}{2\sin\theta} - \dfrac{1}{2} = \dfrac{[\sin(2n+3)\theta]}{2\sin\theta} - \dfrac{1}{2}$
6 Assume q or p odd, $(\sqrt{2} = p/q) \Rightarrow (q\sqrt{2} = p) \Rightarrow (2q^2 = p^2) \Rightarrow (p$ even$) \Rightarrow (p = 2p')$ then $(2q^2 = 4p'^2) \Rightarrow (q^2 = 2p'^2) \Rightarrow (q$ even$)$, contradiction. $(5a-b)\sqrt{2} - (7a-b-c) = 0$. $(5a - b \neq 0) \Rightarrow (\sqrt{2} \in \mathbb{Q})$, hence $5a - b = 0 = 7a - b - c$
7 Induction $3.9^n + 4.2^n = 3(9^n - 2^n) + 7.2^n, 9 - 2$ is a factor of $9^n - 2^n$
8 2 divides $n(n + 1)$, 3 divides $n(n + 1)(n + 2)$
9 $S_1 = 4/(2+1) = 4/(4-1). S_{n+1} = 4n/(2n+1) + 4/[4(n+1)^2 - 1] = 4(n+1)/(2n+3). 0 < 1/[r^2(4r^2-1)] \leqslant 1/(4r^2 - 1)$. Sum $0 < S_n - \displaystyle\sum_{r=1}^{n} 1/r^2 \leqslant \tfrac{1}{4}S_n$
10 Induction, $3^{4n+4} + 2^{4n+5} = 81(3^{4n} + 2^{4n+1}) - 2^{4n+1}.65 \equiv 3.81 \equiv 3 \pmod 5$
11 $(\ln k, k), y = ex, c > e$
12 $f(a_n) \geqslant f\left[\dfrac{a_1 + \ldots + a_{n-1}}{n-1}\right] = \left[\dfrac{a_1 + a_2 + \ldots + a_{n-1}}{(n-1)(a_1 a_2 \ldots a_{n-1})^{1/(n-1)}}\right]^{1-1/n} \geqslant 1^{1-1/n}$
13 (i) True, $(p^2 - q = 7) \Rightarrow (\alpha = -p \pm \sqrt{7}) \Rightarrow (\alpha \in S)$
(ii) False, $\alpha = -6 + 4\sqrt{7}, \beta = -6 - 4\sqrt{7}, p^2 - q = 28$

14 $(3m + 1)^3 \equiv 9(3m^3 + 3m^2 + 3m) + 1$
etc.
$$\sum_{r=1}^{50} r^3 \equiv 1 - 1 + 0 + 1 - 1 + 0 + \ldots +$$
$1 - 1 \equiv 0 \pmod 9$
$x^3 + y^3 + z^3 \equiv \varepsilon_1 + \varepsilon_2 + \varepsilon_3 \not\equiv \pm 4$
(mod 9), where $\varepsilon_i = -1$, 0, or $+1$.
Consider all cases (mod 9)

x	y	z	x^3	y^3	z^3	ε
0	0	0	0	0	0	0
1	1	1	1	1	1	3
2	2	2	8	8	8	6
+ perms 0	1	2	0	1	8	0

15 $m^k x + c\left(\dfrac{m^k - 1}{m - 1}\right),$

$(m^k = 1) \Leftrightarrow (f_k(x) \equiv x)$
Check axioms
16 $N_{2p} - N_{2p-1} = (p - 1)^2,$
$N_{2p+1} - N_{2p} = p(p - 1)$
17 $[\frac{1}{2}n(n + 1)]^2,\ n^2(2n^2 - 1)$
18 $0 \cdot 00712$
22 $\sum c_r^2 = \sum c_r c_{n-r} = $ coeff. of x^n in
$(1 + x)^n (x + 1)^n$
24 $(pqt + rsv)^2 \leqslant (p^2 + r^2)(q^2 t^2 + s^2 v^2)$
25 $10 \cos(\theta + \alpha)$
27 $2^{n+2} + 3^{2n+1} = 2(2^{n+1} + 3^{2n-1}) +$
$3^{2n-1} \cdot 7$ etc.
28 $\dfrac{2n - 1}{4} + \dfrac{\sin(2n + 1)\theta}{4 \sin \theta}$
29 (b) 216, 91; $a = 110,\ b = 70$
30 $20^7,\ 70 \cdot 6^6$
31 (c) Induction, 0, 1, 1, 2, 2, $\ldots$, $(n/2)$,
$\ldots$ or $-1, -1, \ldots, -1, \ldots$
32 $x(ad - bc) = 2d - 3b,$
$y(ad - bc) = 3a - 2c,\ a/c = b/d = 2/3$
33 (a), (d)

Exercise 6
1 $(x < y) \Rightarrow (1/x > 1/y)$ only valid if
$xy > 0$.
2 $\tan x$ not defined when $x = 90°$
3 Series diverges

4 $\displaystyle\int_0^1 1/x^2 \,dx$ diverges

5 $\displaystyle\sum_{r=1}^{\infty} 1/r$ diverges

6 I is not $\ln|t|$ but a set of functions
$\{\ln|t| + c : c \in \mathbb{R}\}$
7 $\int \cot nx \,dx$ is not $\frac{1}{n}\ln|\sin nx|$ but a set
of functions $\{\frac{1}{n}\ln|\sin nx| + c : c \in \mathbb{R}\}$
8 $P(1) \not\Rightarrow P(2)$

Exercise 7.1

1	E	**2**	B	**3**	A	**4**	A
5	D	**6**	B	**7**	C	**8**	B
9	D	**10**	E	**11**	E	**12**	A
13	D	**14**	B	**15**	C	**16**	E
17	C	**18**	B	**19**	B	**20**	D
21	B	**22**	C	**23**	A	**24**	B
25	D	**26**	A	**27**	E	**28**	E
29	B	**30**	C	**31**	D	**32**	C
33	E	**34**	A	**35**	B	**36**	C
37	A	**38**	E	**39**	C	**40**	E
41	E	**42**	A	**43**	B	**44**	D
45	D	**46**	E	**47**	B	**48**	C
49	E	**50**	D	**51**	D	**52**	C
53	D	**54**	A	**55**	B	**56**	C

Exercise 7.2

1	D	**2**	C	**3**	B	**4**	D
5	E	**6**	C	**7**	A	**8**	A
9	C	**10**	C	**11**	B	**12**	A
13	E	**14**	B	**15**	D	**16**	C
17	E	**18**	D	**19**	E	**20**	B
21	C	**22**	C	**23**	B	**24**	C
25	B	**26**	D	**27**	B	**28**	A
29	C	**30**	C	**31**	B	**32**	C
33	A	**34**	E	**35**	A	**36**	B
37	E	**38**	B	**39**	E	**40**	C
41	B	**42**	D	**43**	D	**44**	A
45	C	**46**	B	**47**	A	**48**	C
49	E	**50**	A	**51**	A	**52**	D
53	D	**54**	E	**55**	C	**56**	D
57	D	**58**	B				

Index